Project Development & Documentation (PDD)

ARE 5.0 Mock Exam

(Architect Registration Exam)

ARE 5.0 Overview, Exam Prep Tips,
Hot Spots, Case Studies, Drag-and-Place,
Solutions and Explanations

Gang Chen

ArchiteG®, Inc.
Irvine, California

Project Development & Documentation (PDD) ARE 5.0 Mock Exam (Architect Registration Exam): ARE 5.0 Overview, Exam Prep Tips, Hot Spots, Case Studies, Drag-and-Place, Solutions and Explanations

Copyright © 2017   Gang Chen
V6
Cover Photo © 2017   Gang Chen

Copy Editor: Penny L Kortje

ArchiteG®, Inc.
http://www.ArchiteG.com

ISBN: 9781612650258

PRINTED IN THE UNITED STATES OF AMERICA

What others are saying about *ARE Mock Exam series* …

"Great study guide…"
"This was a great resource supplement to my other study resources. I appreciated the mock exam questions the most, and the solutions offer an explanation as to why the answer is correct. I will definitely check out his other ARE exam resources!

UPDATE: Got my PASS Letter!"
—**Sean Primeaux**

"Tried everything 4 times before reading this book and PASSED!"
"I had failed this exam 4 times prior to getting this book…I had zero clue as to what I was doing wrong. I read Ballast, Kaplan and random things on the forum but for the life of me couldn't pin point where I was missing it until I read THIS BOOK! Gang did an excellent job…I remember going through the ramp and reading Gang's book and saying Ohhhh like 4 or 5 times. I read his book several times until I became comfortable with the information. I went in on test day and it was a breeze. I remember walking out of there thinking I couldn't believe I struggled so much before. The tips in here are priceless! I strongly recommend this book…"
—**hendea1**

"Add this to your ARE study"
"This was a very helpful practice exam and discussion. I really appreciated the step-by-step review of the author's approach... As I studied it last before taking the test, Gang Chen's book probably made the difference for me."
—**Dan Clowes ("XLine")**

"Good supplemental mock exam"
"I found the mock exam to be very helpful, all of the answers are explained thoroughly and really help you understand why it is correct...Also the introduction and test taking tips are very helpful for new candidates just starting the ARE process."
—**Bgrueb01**

"Essential Study Tool"
"I have read the book and found it to be a great study guide for myself. Mr. Gang Chen does such a great job of helping you get into the right frame of mind for the content of the exam. Mr. Chen breaks down the points on what should be studied and how to improve your chances of a pass with his knowledge and tips for the exam and practice vignettes.

I highly recommend this book to anyone…it is an invaluable tool in the preparation for the exam as Mr. Chen provides a vast amount of knowledge in a very clear, concise, and logical matter."
—**Luke Giaccio**

"Wish I had this book earlier"
"...The questions are written like the NCARB questions, with various types...check all that apply, fill in the blank, best answer, etc. The answer key helpfully describes why the correct answer is correct, and why the incorrect answers are not. Take it from my experience, at half the cost of

other mock exams, this is a must buy if you want to pass..."
—**Domiane Forte ("Vitruvian Duck")**

"This book did exactly like the others said."
"This book did exactly like the others said. It is immensely helpful with the explanation... There are so many codes to incorporate, but Chen simplifies it into a methodical process. Bought it and just found out I passed. I would recommend."
—**Dustin**

"It was the reason I passed."
"This book was a huge help. I passed the AREs recently and I felt this book gave me really good explanations for each answer. It was the reason I passed."
—**Amazon Customer**

"Great Practice Exam"
"… For me, it was difficult to not be overwhelmed by the amount of content covered by the Exam. This Mock Exam is the perfect tool to keep you focused on the content that matters and to evaluate what you know and what you need to study. It definitely helped me pass the exam!!"
—**Michael Harvey ("Harv")**

"One of the best practice exams"
"Excellent study guide with study tips, general test info, and recommended study resources. Hands down one of the best practice exams that I have come across for this exam. Most importantly, the practice exam includes in depth explanations of answers. Definitely recommended."
—**Taylor Cupp**

"Great Supplement!!"
"This publication was very helpful in my preparation for my BS exam. It contained a mock exam, followed by the answers and brief explanations to the answers. I would recommend this as an additional study material for this exam."
—**Cynthia Zorrilla-Canteros ("czcante")**

"Fantastic! "
"When I first began to prepare for this exam; the number of content areas seemed overwhelming and daunting at best. However, this guide clearly dissected each content area into small management components. Of all the study guides currently available for this test - this exam not only included numerous resources (web links, you tube clips, etc..), but also the sample test was extremely helpful. The sample test incorporated a nice balance of diagrams, calculations and general concepts - this book allowed me to highlight any "weak" content areas I had prior to the real exam. In short - this is an awesome book!"
—**Rachel Casey (RC)**

Dedication

To my parents, Zhuixian and Yugen,
my wife, Xiaojie, and my daughters,
Alice, Angela, Amy, and Athena.

Disclaimer

Project Development & Documentation (PDD) ARE 5.0 Mock Exam (Architect Registration Exam) provides general information about Architect Registration Examination. The book is sold with the understanding that neither the publisher nor the authors are providing legal, accounting, or other professional services. If legal, accounting, or other professional services are required, seek the assistance of a competent professional firm.

The purpose of this publication is not to reprint the content of all other available texts on the subject. You are urged to read other materials, and tailor them to fit your needs.

Great effort has been taken to make this resource as complete and accurate as possible. However, nobody is perfect and there may be typographical errors or other mistakes present. You should use this book as a general guide and not as the ultimate source on this subject. If you find any potential errors, please send an e-mail to:
info@ArchiteG.com

Project Development & Documentation (PDD) ARE 5.0 Mock Exam (Architect Registration Exam) is intended to provide general, entertaining, informative, educational, and enlightening content. Neither the publisher nor the author shall be liable to anyone or any entity for any loss or damages, or alleged loss or damages, caused directly or indirectly by the content of this book.

ArchiteG®, Green Associate Exam Guide®, GA Study®, and GreenExamEducation® are registered trademarks owned by Gang Chen.

ARE®, Architect Registration Examination® are registered trademarks owned by NCARB.

If you do not wish to be bound by the above, you may return this book to the publisher for a full refund.

Legal Notice

ARE Mock Exam series by ArchiteG, Inc.

Time and effort is the most valuable asset of a candidate. How to cherish and effectively use your limited time and effort is the key of passing any exam. That is why we publish the ARE Mock Exam series to help you to study and pass the ARE exams in the shortest time possible. We have done the hard work so that you can save time and money. We do not want to make you work harder than you have to. To save your time, we use a *standard* format for all our ARE 5.0 Mock Exam books, so that you can quickly skip the *identical* information you have already read in other books of the series, and go straight to the *unique* "meat and potatoes" portion of the book.

The trick and the most difficult part of writing a good book is to turn something that is very complicated into something that is very simple. This involves researching and really understanding some very complicated materials, absorbing the information, and then writing about the topic in a way that makes it very easy to understand. To succeed at this, you need to know the materials very well. Our goal is to write books that are clear, concise, and helpful to anyone with a seventh-grade education.

Do not force yourself to memorize a lot of numbers. Read through the numbers a few times, and you should have a very good impression of them.

You need to make the judgment call: If you miss a few numbers, you can still pass the exam, but if you spend too much time drilling these numbers, you may miss out on the big pictures and fail the exam.

The existing ARE practice questions or exams by others are either way too easy or way over-killed. They do NOT match the real ARE 5.0 exams at all.

We have done very comprehensive research on the official NCARB guides, many related websites, reference materials, and other available ARE exam prep materials. We match our mock exams as close as possible to the NCARB samples and the real ARE exams instead. Some readers had failed an ARE exam two or three times before, and they eventually passed the exam with our help.

All our books include a complete set of questions and case studies. We try to mimic the real ARE exams by including the same number of questions, using a similar format, and asking the same type of questions. We also include detailed answers and explanations to our questions.

There is some extra information on ARE overviews and exam-taking tips in Chapter One. This is based on NCARB *and* other valuable sources. This is a bonus feature we included in each book because we want our readers to be able to buy our ARE mock exam books together or individually. We want you to find all necessary ARE exam information and resources at one place and through our books.

All our books are available at
http://www.GreenExamEducation.com

How to Use This Book

We suggest you read *Project Development & Documentation (PDD) ARE 5.0 Mock Exam (Architect Registration Exam)* at least three times:

Read once and cover Chapter One and Two, the Appendixes, the related *free* PDF files, and other resources. Highlight the information you are not familiar with.

Read twice focusing on the highlighted information to memorize. You can repeat this process as many times as you want until you master the content of the book.

After reviewing these materials, you can take the mock exam, and then check your answers against the answers and explanations in the back, including explanations for the questions you answer correctly. You may have answered some questions correctly for the wrong reason. Highlight the information you are not familiar with.

Like the real exam, the mock exam will continue to use **multiple choice, check-all-that-apply,** and **quantitative fill-in-the-blank**. There are also three new question types: **hot spots, case studies,** and **drag-and-place**.

Review your highlighted information, and take the mock exam again. Try to answer 100% of the questions correctly this time. Repeat the process until you can answer all the questions correctly.

PDD is one of the most difficult ARE divisions because many PDD questions require calculations. This book includes most if not all the information you need to do the calculations, as well as step-by-step explanations. After reading this book, you will greatly improve your ability to deal with the real ARE PDD calculations, and have a great chance of passing the exam on the first try.

Take the mock exam at least two weeks before the real exam. You should definitely NOT wait until the night before the real exam to take the mock exam. If you do not do well, you will go into panic mode and NOT have enough time to review your weaknesses.

Read for the final time the night before the real exam. Review ONLY the information you highlighted, especially the questions you did not answer correctly when you took the mock exam for the first time.

This book is very light so you can easily carry it around. These features will allow you to review the graphic vignette section whenever you have a few minutes.

The Table of Contents is very detailed so you can locate information quickly. If you are on a tight schedule you can forgo reading the book linearly and jump around to the sections you need.

All our books, including "ARE Mock Exams Series" and "LEED Exam Guides Series," are available at

GreenExamEducation.com

Check out FREE tips and info at **GeeForum.com**, you can post your questions for other users' review and responses.

Table of Contents

Chapter One   Overview of Architect Registration Examination (ARE)

   1. Important links to the FREE and official NCARB documents
   2. A detailed list and brief description of the FREE PDF files that you can download from NCARB
      • ARE 5.0 Credit Model
      • ARE 5.0 Guidelines
      • NCARB Education Guidelines
      • Architectural Experience Program (AXP) Guidelines
      • Certification Guidelines
      • ARE 5.0 Related FAQs (Frequently Asked Questions)
      • Your Guide to ARE 5.0
      • ARE 5.0 Handbook
      • ARE 5.0 Test Specification
      • ARE 5.0 Prep Videos
      • The Burning Question: Why Do We need ARE anyway?
      • Defining Your Moral Compass
      • Rules of Conduct

   1. What is IDP? What is AXP?
   2. Who qualifies as an intern?

1. How to qualify for the ARE?
2. How to qualify for an architect license?
3. What is the purpose of ARE?
4. What is NCARB's rolling clock?
5. How to register for an ARE exam?
6. How early do I need to arrive at the test center?
7. Exam Format & Time
    *   Practice Management (PcM)
    *   Project Management (PjM)
    *   Programming & Analysis (PA)
    *   Project Planning & Design (PPD)
    *   Project Development & Documentation (PDD)
    *   Construction & Evaluation (CE)
8. How are ARE scores reported?
9. Is there a fixed percentage of candidates who pass the ARE exams?
10. When can I retake a failed ARE division?
11. How much time do I need to prepare for each ARE division?
12. Which ARE division should I take first?
13. ARE exam prep and test-taking tips
14. Strategies for passing ARE exams on the first try
    *   Find out how much you already know and what you should study
    *   Cherish and effectively use your limited time and effort
    *   Do NOT stretch your exam prep process too long
    *   Resist the temptation to read many books and limit your time and effort to read only a few selected books or a few sections of books in details
    *   Think like an architect.
15. ARE exam preparation requires short-term memory
16. Allocation of your time and scheduling
17. Timing of review: the 3016 rule; memorization methods, tips, suggestions, and mnemonics
18. The importance of good and effective study methods
19. The importance of repetition: read this book <u>at least</u> three times
20. The importance of a routine
21. The importance of short, frequent breaks and physical exercise
22. A strong vision and a clear goal
23. English system (English or inch-pound units) vs. metric system (SI units)
24. Codes and standards used in this book
25. Where can I find study materials on architectural history?

Back Page Promotion

Index

Chapter One

Overview of the Architect Registration Examination (ARE)

A. First Thing First: Go to the Website of your Architect Registration Board and Read all the Requirements of Obtaining an Architect License in your Jurisdiction
See the following link:
http://www.ncarb.org/Getting-an-Initial-License/Registration-Board-Requirements.aspx

B. Download and Review the Latest ARE Documents at the NCARB Website

1. Important links to the FREE and official NCARB documents
NCARB launched ARE 5.0 on November 1, 2016. ARE 4.0 will continue to be available until June 30, 2018.

ARE candidates who started testing in ARE 4.0 can choose to "self-transition" to ARE 5.0. This will allow them to continue testing in the version that is most suitable for them. However, **once a candidate transitions to ARE 5.0, s/he cannot transition back to ARE 4.0**.

The current version of the Architect Registration Examination (ARE 5.0) includes six divisions:

- Practice Management (PcM)
- Project Management (PjM)
- Programming & Analysis (PA)
- Project Planning & Design (PPD)
- Project Development & Documentation (PDD)
- Construction & Evaluation (CE)

All ARE divisions continue to use **multiple choice, check-all-that-apply,** and **quantitative fill-in-the-blank**. The new exams include three new question types: **hot spots, case studies,** and **drag-and-place**.

There is a tremendous amount of valuable information covering every step of becoming an architect available free of charge at the NCARB website:
http://www.ncarb.org/

For example, you can find guidance about architectural degree programs accredited by the National Architectural Accrediting Board (NAAB), NCARB's Architectural Experience Program (AXP) formerly known as Intern Development Program (IDP), and licensing requirements by state. These documents explain how you can qualify to take the Architect Registration Examination.

We find the official ARE 5.0 Guidelines, ARE 5.0 Handbook, and ARE 5.0 Credit Model extremely valuable. See the following link:
http://www.ncarb.org/ARE/ARE5.aspx

You should start by studying these documents.

2. **A detailed list and brief description of the FREE PDF files that you can download from NCARB**
   The following is a detailed list of the FREE PDF files that you can download from NCARB. They are listed in order based on their importance.

   - All **ARE 5.0** information can be found at the following links:
     http://www.ncarb.org/ARE/ARE5.aspx
     http://blog.ncarb.org/2016/November/ARE5-Study-Materials.aspx
   - The **ARE 5.0 Credit Model** is one of the most important documents, and tells you the easiest way to pass the ARE by taking selected divisions from ARE 4.0 and ARE 5.0.

ARE5.0:	Practice Management	Project Management	Programming & Analysis	Project Planning & Design	Project Development & Documentation	Construction & Evaluation
ARE 4.0:						
Construction Documents & Services	●	●			●	●
Programming Planning & Practice	●	●	●			
Site Planning & Design			●	●		
Building Design & Construction Systems				●	●	
Structural Systems				●	●	
Building Systems				●	●	
Schematic Design				●		

As shown in matrix above, if you are taking both ARE 4.0 and ARE 5.0, you can pass the ARE exams by taking only five divisions in total. To complete the ARE, your goal is to select and pass exams from both versions which cover all sixteen dots in matrix above. The quickest potential options are as follows:

a. You can take the following five divisions to pass the ARE:
ARE 4.0
- Construction Documents & Services
- Programming Planning & Practice
- Site Planning & Design

ARE 5.0
- Project Planning & Design
- Project Development & Documentation

OR

b. You can take the following five divisions to pass the ARE:
ARE 4.0
- Construction Documents & Services
- Programming Planning & Practice

ARE 5.0
- Programming & Analysis
- Project Planning & Design
- Project Development & Documentation

- **ARE 5.0 Guidelines** includes extremely valuable information on the ARE overview, NCARB, registration (licensure), architectural education requirements, the Architectural Experience Program (AXP), establishing your eligibility to test, scheduling an exam appointment, taking the ARE, receiving your score, retaking the ARE, the exam format, scheduling, and links to other FREE NCARB PDF files. You need to read this <u>at least twice</u>.

- **NCARB Education Guidelines** contains information on education requirements for initial licensure and for NCARB certification, satisfying the education requirement, foreign-educated applicants, the education alternative to NCARB certification, the Education Evaluation Services for Architects (EESA), the Education Standard, and other resources.

- **Architectural Experience Program (AXP) Guidelines** includes information on AXP overview, getting started and creating your NCARB record, experience areas and tasks, documenting your experience through hours, documenting your experience through a portfolio, and the next steps. You need to read this document <u>at least twice</u>. The information is valuable.

  NCARB renamed the **Intern Development Program (IDP)** as **Architectural Experience Program (AXP)** in June 2016. Most of NCARB's 54-member boards have adopted the AXP as a prerequisite for initial architect licensure. Therefore, you should be familiar with the program.

The AXP application fee is $100. This fee includes one free transmittal of your Record for initial registration and keeps your Record active for the first year. After the initial year, there is an annual renewal fee required to maintain an active Record until you become registered. The cost is currently $85 each year. The fees are subject to change, and you need to check the NCARB website for the latest information.

There are two ways to meet the AXP requirements. The **first method** is **reporting hours**. Most candidates will use this method. You will need to document at least 3,740 required hours under the six different experience areas to complete the program. A minimum of 50% of your experience must be completed under the supervision of a qualified architect.

The following chart lists the hours required under the six experience areas:

Experience Area	Hours Required
Practice Management	160
Project Management	360
Programming & Analysis	260
Project Planning & Design	1,080
Project Development & Documentation	1,520
Construction & Evaluation	360
Total	**3,740**

Your experience reports will fall under one of **two experience settings**:
• **Setting A**: Work performed for an architecture firm.
• **Setting O**: Experiences performed outside an architecture firm.

You must earn at least **1,860 hours** in experience **setting A**.

Your AXP experience <u>should be reported to NCARB at least every six months</u> and logged within two months of completing each reporting period (the **Six-Month Rule**).

The **second method** to meet AXP requirements is to create an **AXP Portfolio**. This new method is for experienced design professionals who put their licensure on hold and allows you to prove your experience through the preparation of an online portfolio.

To complete the AXP through the **second method**, you will need to meet ALL the AXP criteria through the portfolio. In other words, you cannot complete the experience requirement through a combination of the **AXP portfolio** and **reporting hours**.

See the following link for more information on AXP:
http://www.ncarb.org/Experience-Through-Internships.aspx

• **Certification Guidelines** by NCARB (Skimming through this should be adequate. You should also forward a copy of this PDF file to your IDP supervisor.)

See the following link which contains resources for supervisors and mentors:
http://www.ncarb.org/Experience-Through-Internships/Supervisors-and-Mentors/Resources-for-Supervisor-and-Mentors.aspx

- **ARE 5.0 Related FAQs (Frequently Asked Questions)**: Skimming through this should be adequate.

- **Your Guide to ARE 5.0** includes information on understanding the basics of ARE 5.0, new question types, taking the test, making the transition, getting ARE 5.0 done, and planning your budget. The document also contains FAQs, and links for more information. You need to read this document <u>at least twice</u>. The information is valuable.

- **ARE 5.0 Handbook** contains an ARE overview, detailed information for each ARE division, and ARE 5.0 references. This handbook explains what NCARB expects you to know so that you can pass the ARE exams. ARE 5.0 uses either **Understand/Apply (U/A)** or **Analyze/Evaluate (A/E)** to designate the appropriate cognitive complexity of each objective, but *avoids* the use of **"Remember,"** the lowest level of cognitive complexity (CC), or **"Create,"** the highest level of CC.

  This handbook has some sample questions for each division. The real exam is like the samples in this handbook.

  Tips:
  - *ARE 5.0 Handbook has about 170 pages. To save time, you can just read the generic information at the front and back portion of the handbook, and focus on the ARE division(s) you are currently studying for. As you progress in your testing you can read the applicable division that you are studying for. This way the content will always be fresh in your mind.*
  - *You need to read this document <u>at least three times</u>. The information is valuable.*

- **ARE 5.0 Test Specification** identifies the ARE 5.0 division structure and defines the major content areas, called **Sections**; the measurement **Objectives**; and the percentage of content coverage, called **Weightings**. This document specifies the scope and objectives of each ARE division, and the percentage of questions in each content category. You need to read this document <u>at least twice</u>. The information is valuable, and is the base of all ARE exam questions.

- **ARE 5.0 Prep Videos** include one short video for each division. These videos give you a very good basic introduction to each division, including sample questions and answers, and explanations. You need to watch each video <u>at least three times</u>. See the following link:
  http://blog.ncarb.org/2016/November/ARE5-Study-Materials.aspx

- **The Burning Question: Why Do We Need ARE Anyway?** (We do not want to give out a link for this document because it is too long and keeps changing. You can Google it with its title. Skimming through this document should be adequate.)

- **Defining Your Moral Compass** (You can Google it with its title plus the word "NCARB." Skimming through this document should be adequate.)

- **Rules of Conduct** is available as a FREE PDF file at:
  http://www.ncarb.org/
  (Skimming through this should be adequate.)

C. The Intern Development Program (IDP)/Architectural Experience Program (AXP)

1. What is IDP? What is AXP?
IDP is a comprehensive training program jointly developed by the National Council of Architectural Registration Boards (NCARB) and the American Institute of Architects (AIA) to ensure that interns obtain the necessary skills and knowledge to practice architecture <u>independently</u>. NCARB renamed the **Intern Development Program (IDP)** as **Architectural Experience Program (AXP)** in June 2016.

2. Who qualifies as an intern?
Per NCARB, if an individual meets one of the following criteria, s/he qualifies as an intern:
a. Graduates from NAAB-accredited programs
b. Architecture students who acquire acceptable training prior to graduation
c. Other qualified individuals identified by a registration board

D. Overview of the Architect Registration Examination (ARE)

1. How to qualify for the ARE?
A candidate needs to qualify for the ARE via one of NCARB's member registration boards, or one of the Canadian provincial architectural associations.

Check with your Board of Architecture for specific requirements.

For example, in California, a candidate must provide verification of a minimum of <u>five</u> years of education and/or architectural work experience to qualify for the ARE.

Candidates can satisfy the five-year requirement in a variety of ways:

- Provide verification of a professional degree in architecture through a program that is accredited by NAAB or CACB.

  OR
- Provide verification of at least five years of educational equivalents.

  OR
- Provide proof of work experience under the direct supervision of a licensed architect

See the following link:
http://www.ncarb.org/ARE/Getting-Started-With-the-ARE/Ready-to-Take-the-ARE-Early.aspx

2. **How to qualify for an architect license?**

Again, each jurisdiction has its own requirements. An individual typically needs a combination of about <u>eight</u> years of education and experience, as well as passing scores on the ARE exams. See the following link:
http://www.ncarb.org/Reg-Board-Requirements

For example, the requirements to become a licensed architect in California are:
- Eight years of post-secondary education and/or work experience as evaluated by the Board (including at least one year of work experience under the direct supervision of an architect licensed in a U.S. jurisdiction or two years of work experience under the direct supervision of an architect registered in a Canadian province)
- Completion of the Architectural Experience Program (AXP)
- Successful completion of the Architect Registration Examination (ARE)
- Successful completion of the California Supplemental Examination (CSE)

California does NOT require an accredited degree in architecture for examination and licensure. However, many other states do.

3. **What is the purpose of ARE?**

The purpose of ARE is NOT to test a candidate's competency on every aspect of architectural practice. Its purpose is to test a candidate's competency on providing professional services to protect the <u>health, safety, and welfare</u> of the public. It tests candidates on the <u>fundamental</u> knowledge of pre-design, site design, building design, building systems, and construction documents and services.

The ARE tests a candidate's competency as a "specialist" on architectural subjects. It also tests her abilities as a "generalist" to coordinate other consultants' works.

You can download the exam content and references for each of the ARE divisions at the following links:
http://www.ncarb.org/ARE/ARE5.aspx
http://www.ncarb.org/are/40/StudyAids.html

4. **What is NCARB's rolling clock?**
   a. Starting on January 1, 2006, a candidate MUST pass ALL ARE sections within five years. A passing score for an ARE division is only valid for five years, and a candidate has to retake this division if she has NOT passed all divisions within the five-year period.

   b. Starting on January 1, 2011, a candidate who is authorized to take ARE exams MUST take at least one division of the ARE exams within five years of the authorization.

Otherwise, the candidate MUST apply for the authorization to take ARE exams from an NCARB member board again.

These rules were created by the **NCARB's rolling clock** resolution and passed by NCARB council during the 2004 NCARB Annual Meeting.

ARE 4.0 division expiration dates per the Rolling Clock will remain the same for the transition to ARE 5.0.

5. **How to register for an ARE exam?**
   See the instructions in the new ARE guideline at the following link:
   http://www.ncarb.org/ARE/ARE5.aspx

6. **How early do I need to arrive at the test center?**
   Be at the test center at least 30 minutes BEFORE your scheduled test time, OR you may lose your exam fee.

7. **Exam format & time**
   All ARE divisions are administered and graded by computer. Their time allowances are as follows:

Division	Number of Questions	Test Duration	Appointment Time
Practice Management	80	2 hr 45 min	3 hr 30 min
Project Management	95	3 hr 15 min	4 hr
Programming & Analysis	95	3 hr 15 min	4 hr
Project Planning & Design	120	4 hr 15 min	5 hr
Project Development & Documentation	120	4 hr 15 min	5 hr
Construction & Evaluation	95	3 hr 15 min	4 hr
Total Time:		21 hr	25 hr 30 min

NCARB suggests you to arrive at the test center a minimum of 30 minutes before your scheduled appointment. You can have one flexible 15-minute break for each division. That is why the appointment time is 45 minutes longer than the actual test time for each division.

Practice Management has 80 questions and NCARB allows you 2 hours and 45 minutes to complete the exam, so you should spend an average of (2x60+45)/80=165/80= 2.06 minutes on each question.

Project Management and **Programming & Analysis** as well as **Construction & Evaluation** each have 95 questions and NCARB allows you 3 hours and 15 minutes to complete each exam, so you should spend an average of (3x60+15)/80=195/95= 2.05 minutes on each question.

Project Planning & Design as well as **Project Development & Documentation** each have 120 questions and NCARB allows you 4 hours and 15 minutes to complete each exam, so you should spend an average of (4x60+15)/120=255/120= 2.13 minutes on each question.

To simplify this, we suggest you spend about 2 minutes for each question in ALL divisions.

8. How are ARE scores reported?
All ARE scores are reported as Pass or Fail. ARE scores are typically posted within 7 to 10 days. See the instructions in the new ARE guideline at the following link: http://www.ncarb.org/ARE/ARE5.aspx

9. Is there a fixed percentage of candidates who pass the ARE exams?
No, there is NOT a fixed percentage of passing or failing. If you meet the minimum competency required to practice as an architect, you pass. The passing scores are the same for all Boards of Architecture.

10. When can I retake a failed ARE division?
You can retake a failed division of the ARE 60 days after the previous attempt. You can only take the same ARE division three (3) times within any 12-month period.

11. How much time do I need to prepare for each ARE division?
Every person is different, but on average you need about 40 to 80 hours to prepare for each ARE division. You need to set a realistic study schedule and stick with it. Make sure you allow time for personal and recreational commitments. If you are working full time, my suggestion is that you allow no less than 2 weeks but NOT more than 2 months to prepare for each ARE division. You should NOT drag out the exam prep process too long and risk losing your momentum.

12. Which ARE division should I take first?
This is a matter of personal preference, and you should make the final decision.

Some people like to start with the easier divisions and pass them first. This way, they build more confidence as they study and pass each division.

Other people like to start with the more difficult divisions so that if they fail, they can keep busy studying and taking the other divisions while the clock is ticking. Before they know it, six months has passed and they can reschedule if need be.

13. ARE exam prep and test-taking tips
You can start with Construction & Evaluation (CE) because it gives a limited scope, and you may want to study building regulations and architectural history (especially famous architects and buildings that set the trends at critical turning points) before you take other divisions.

Complete mock exams and practice questions and vignettes, including those provided by NCARB's practice program and this book, to hone your skills.

Form study groups and learn the exam experience of other ARE candidates. The forum at our website is a helpful resource. See the following links:
http://GreenExamEducation.com/
http://GeeForum.com/

Take the ARE exams as soon as you become eligible, since you probably still remember portions of what you learned in architectural school, especially structural and architectural history. Do not make excuses for yourself and put off the exams.

The following test-taking tips may help you:
- Pace yourself properly. You should spend about two minutes for each question on average.
- Read the questions carefully and pay attention to words like *best, could, not, always, never, seldom, may, false, except,* etc.
- For questions that you are not sure of, eliminate the obvious wrong answer and then make an educated guess. Please note that if you do NOT answer the question, you automatically lose the point. If you guess, you at least have a chance to get it right.
- If you have no idea what the correct answer is and cannot eliminate any obvious wrong answers, then do not waste too much time on the question and just guess. Try to use the same guess answer for all of the questions you have no idea about. For example, if you choose "d" as the guess answer, then you should be consistent and use "d" whenever you have no clue. This way, you are likely have a better chance at guessing more answers correctly.
- Mark the difficult questions, answer them, and come back to review them AFTER you finish all MC questions. If you are still not sure, go with your first choice. Your first choice is often the best choice.
- You really need to spend time practicing to become VERY familiar with NCARB's question types. This is because ARE is a timed test, and you do NOT have time to learn about the question types during the test. If you do not know them well, you will NOT be able to finish your solution to the vignette on time.
- The ARE exams test a candidate's competency to provide professional services protecting the <u>health, safety, and welfare</u> of the public. Do NOT waste time on aesthetic or other design elements not required by the program.

ARE exams are difficult, but if you study hard and prepare well, combined with your experience, AXP training, and/or college education, you should be able to pass all divisions and eventually be able to call yourself an architect.

14. Strategies for passing ARE exams on the first try
Passing ARE exams on the first try, like everything else, needs not only hard work, but also great strategy.

- **Find out how much you already know and what you should study**

  You goal is NOT to read all the study materials. Your goal is to pass the exam. Flip through the study materials. If you already know the information, skip these parts.

  Complete the NCARB sample questions for the ARE exam you are preparing for NOW without ANY studying. See what percentage you get right. If you get 60% right, you should be able to pass the real exam without any studying. If you get 50% right, then you just need 10% more to pass.

  This "truth-finding" exam or exercise will also help you to find out what your weakness areas are, and what to focus on.

  Look at the same questions again at the end of your exam prep, and check the differences.

  Note: We suggest you study the sample questions in the official NCARB Study Guide first, and then other study materials, and then come back to NCARB sample questions again several days before the real ARE exam.

- **Cherish and effectively use your limited time and effort**

  Let me paraphrase a story.
  One time someone had a chance to talk with Napoleon. He said:
  "You are such a great leader and have won so many battles, that you can use one of your soldiers to defeat ten enemy soldiers."

  Napoleon responded:
  "That may be true, but I always try to create opportunities where ten of my soldiers fight one enemy soldier. That is why I have won so many battles."

  Whether this story is true is irrelevant. The important thing that you need to know is **how to concentrate your limited time and effort to achieve your goal. Do NOT spread yourself too thin**. This is a principle many great leaders know and use and is why great leaders can use ordinary people to achieve extraordinary goals.

  Time and effort is the most valuable asset of a candidate. How to cherish and effectively use your limited time and effort is the key to passing any exam.

  If you study very hard and read many books, you are probably wasting your time. You are much better off picking one or two good books, covering the major framework of your exams, and then doing two sets of mock exams to find your weaknesses. You WILL pass if you follow this advice. You may still have minor weakness, but you will have covered your major bases.

- **Do NOT stretch your exam prep process too long**
  If you do this, it will hurt instead of help you. You may forget the information by the time you take the exam.

  Spend 40 to 80 hours for each division (a maximum of two months for the most difficult exams if you really need more time) should be enough. Once you decide on taking an exam, put in 100% of your effort and read the RIGHT materials. Allocate your time and effort on the most important materials, and you will pass.

- **Resist the temptation to read too many books and limit your time and effort to read only a few selected books or a few sections of each book in detail**
  Having all the books but not reading them, or digesting ALL the information in them will not help you. It is like someone having a garage full of foods, and not eating or eating too much of them. Neither way will help.

  You can only eat three meals a day. Similarly, you can ONLY absorb a certain amount of information during your exam prep. So, focus on the most important stuff.

  Focus on your weaknesses but still read the other info. The key is to understand, digest the materials, and retain the information.

  It is NOT how much you have read, but how much you understand, digest, and retain that counts.

  The key to passing an ARE exam, or any other exam, is to know the scope of the exam, and not to read too many books. Select one or two really good books and focus on them. Actually <u>understand</u> the content and <u>memorize</u> it. For your convenience, I have <u>underlined</u> the fundamental information that I think is very important. You definitely need to <u>memorize</u> all the information that I have underlined.

  You should try to understand the content first, and then memorize the content of the book by reading it multiple times. This is a much better way than relying on "mechanical" memory without understanding.

  When you read the materials, ALWAYS keep the following in mind:

- **Think like an architect.**
  For example, when you take the Project Development & Documentation (PDD) exam, focus on what need to know to be able to coordinate your engineer's work, or tell them what to do. You are NOT taking an exam for becoming a structural engineer; you are taking an exam to become an architect.

  This criterion will help you filter out the materials that are irrelevant, and focus on the right information. You will know what to flip through, what to read line by line, and what to read multiple times.

I have said this one thousand times, and I will say it once more:
Time and effort is the most valuable asset of a candidate. How to cherish and effectively use your limited time and effort is the key to passing any exam.

15. ARE exam preparation requires short-term memory

You should understand that ARE Exam Preparation requires **Short-Term Memory**. This is especially true for the MC portion of the exam. You should schedule your time accordingly: in the <u>early</u> stages of your ARE exam Preparation, you should focus on <u>understanding</u> and an **initial** review of the material; in the <u>late</u> stages of your exam preparation, you should focus on <u>memorizing</u> the material as a **final** review.

16. Allocation of your time and scheduling

You should spend about 60% of your effort on the most important and fundamental study materials, about 30% of your effort on mock exams, and the remaining 10% on improving your weakest areas, i.e., reading and reviewing the questions that you answered incorrectly, reinforcing the portions that you have a hard time memorizing, etc.

Do NOT spend too much time looking for <u>obscure</u> ARE information because the NCARB will *have* to test you on the most **common** architectural knowledge and information. At least <u>80% to 90%</u> of the exam content will have to be the most <u>common</u>, <u>important</u> and <u>fundamental</u> knowledge. The exam writers can word their questions to be <u>tricky</u> or <u>confusing</u>, but they have to limit themselves to the <u>important</u> content; otherwise, their tests will NOT be legally defensible. At most, <u>10%</u> of their test content can be <u>obscure</u> information. You only need to answer about 60% of all the questions correctly. So, if you master the common ARE knowledge (applicable to 90% of the questions) and use the guess technique for the remaining 10% of the questions on the obscure ARE content, you will do well and pass the exam.

On the other hand, if you focus on the obscure ARE knowledge, you may answer the entire 10% <u>obscure</u> portion of the exam correctly, but only answer half of the remaining 90% of the <u>common</u> ARE knowledge questions correctly, and you will fail the exam. That is why we have seen many smart people who can answer very difficult ARE questions correctly because they are able to look them up and do quality research. However, they often end up failing ARE exams because they cannot memorize the common ARE knowledge needed on the day of the exam. ARE exams are NOT an open-book exams, and you cannot look up information during the exam.

The **process of memorization** is like **<u>filling a cup with a hole at the bottom</u>**: You need to fill it <u>faster</u> than the water leaks out at the bottom, and you need to <u>constantly</u> fill it; otherwise, it will quickly be empty.

Once you memorize something, your brain has already started the process of forgetting it. It is natural. That is how we have enough space left in our brain to remember the really important things.

It is tough to fight against your brain's natural tendency to forget things. Acknowledging this truth and the fact that you ca<u>nnot</u> memorize everything you read, you need to <u>focus</u> your limited time, energy and brainpower on the <u>most important</u> issues.

The biggest danger for most people is that they memorize the information in the early stages of their exam preparation, but forget it before or on the day of the exam and still THINK they remember them.

Most people fail the exam NOT because they cannot answer the few "advanced" questions on the exam, but because they have read the information but can <u>NOT</u> recall it on the day of the exam. They spend too much time preparing for the exam, drag the preparation process on too long, seek too much information, go to too many websites, do too many practice questions and too many mock exams (one or two sets of mock exams can be good for you), and **spread themselves too thin**. They end up **missing the most important information** of the exam, and they will fail.

The ARE Mock Exam series along with the tips and methodology in each of the books will help you find and improvement your weakness areas, MEMORIZE the most important aspects of the test to pass the exam ON THE FIRST TRY.

So, if you have a lot of time to prepare for the ARE exams, you should plan your effort accordingly. You want your ARE knowledge to peak at the time of the exam, not before or after.

For example, <u>if you have two months to prepare for a very difficult ARE exam</u>, you may want to spend the first month focused on <u>reading and understanding</u> all of the study materials you can find as your **initial** review. Also during this first month, you can start <u>memorizing</u> after you understand the materials as long as you know you HAVE to review the materials again later to <u>retain</u> them. If you have memorized something once, it is easier to memorize it again later.

Next, you can spend two weeks focused on <u>memorizing</u> the material. You need to review the material at least three times. You can then spend one week on <u>mock exams</u>. The last week before the exam, focus on retaining your knowledge and reinforcing your weakest areas. Read the mistakes that you have made and think about how to avoid them during the real exam. Set aside a mock exam that you <u>have not taken</u> and take it seven days before test day. This will alert you to your weaknesses and provide direction for the remainder of your studies.

<u>If you have one week to prepare for the exam</u>, you can spend two days reading and understanding the study material, two days repeating and memorizing the material, two days on mock exams, and one day retaining the knowledge and enforcing your weakest areas.

The last one to two weeks before an exam is <u>absolutely</u> critical. You need to have the "do or die" mentality and be ready to study hard to pass the exam on your first try. That is how some people are able to pass an ARE exam with only one week of preparation.

17. Timing of review: the 3016 rule; memorization methods, tips, suggestions, and mnemonics

Another important strategy is to review the material in a timely manner. Some people say that the best time to <u>review</u> material is between <u>30 minutes and 16 hours</u> (the **3016** rule) after you read it for the first time. So, if you review the material right after you read it for the first time, the review may not be helpful.

I have personally found this method extremely beneficial. The best way for me to memorize study materials is to review what I learn during the day again in the evening. This, of course, happens to fall within the timing range mentioned above.

Now that you know the **3016** rule, you may want to schedule your review accordingly. For example, you may want to read <u>new</u> study materials in the morning and afternoon, then after dinner do an <u>initial review</u> of what you learned during the day.

OR

If you are working full time, you can read <u>new</u> study materials in the evening or at night and then get up early the next morning to spend one or two hours on an <u>initial review</u> of what you learned the night before.

The <u>initial</u> review and memorization will make your <u>final</u> review and memorization much easier.

Mnemonics is a very good way for you to memorize facts and data that are otherwise very hard to memorize. It is often <u>arbitrary</u> or <u>illogical</u> but it works.

A good mnemonic can help you remember something for a long time or even a lifetime after reading it just once. Without the mnemonics, you may read the same thing many times and still not be able to memorize it.

There are a few common Mnemonics:
1) **<u>Visual</u>** Mnemonics: Link what you want to memorize to a visual image.
2) **<u>Spatial</u>** Mnemonics: link what you want to memorize to a space, and the order of things in it.
3) **<u>Group</u>** Mnemonics: <u>Break up</u> a difficult piece <u>into</u> several smaller and more <u>manageable groups or sets</u>, and memorize the sets and their order. One example is the grouping of the 10-digit phone number into three groups in the U.S. This makes the number much easier to memorize.
4) **<u>Architectural</u>** Mnemonics: A combination of <u>Visual</u> Mnemonics and <u>Spatial</u> Mnemonics and <u>Group</u> Mnemonics.

Imagine you are walking through a building several times, along the same path. You should be able to remember the order of each room. You can then break up the information that you want to remember and link them to several images, and then imagine you hang the images on walls of various rooms. You should be able to easily recall each group in an orderly manner by imagining you are walking through the building again on the same path, and looking at the images hanging on walls of each room. When you look at the images on the wall, you can easily recall the related information.

You can use your home, office or another building that you are <u>familiar with</u> to build an <u>Architectural</u> Mnemonics to help you to organize the things you need to memorize.

5) **<u>Association</u>** Mnemonics: You can <u>associate</u> what you want to memorize <u>with a sentence</u>, a similarly pronounced word, or a place you are familiar with, etc.
6) **<u>Emotion</u>** Mnemonics: Use emotion to fix an image in your memory.
7) **<u>First Letter</u>** Mnemonics: You can use the <u>first letter</u> of what you want to memorize <u>to construct a sentence or acronym</u>. For example, "**Roy G. Biv**" can be used to memorize the order of the 7 colors of the rainbow, it is composed of the first letter of each primary color.

You can use **<u>Association</u>** Mnemonics and memorize them as <u>all</u> the plumbing fixtures for a typical home, PLUS Urinal.

OR
You can use "Water S K U L" (**<u>First Letter</u>** Mnemonics selected from website below) to memorize them:

<u>W</u>ater Closets
<u>S</u>hower
<u>K</u>itchen Sinks
<u>U</u>rinal
<u>L</u>avatory

18. The importance of good and effective study methods
There is a saying: Give a man a fish, feed him for a day. Teach a man to fish, feed him for a lifetime. I think there is some truth to this. Similarly, it is better to teach someone HOW to study than just give him good study materials. In this book, I give you good study materials to save you time, but more importantly, I want to teach you effective study methods so that you can not only study and pass ARE exams, but also so that you will benefit throughout the rest of your life for anything else you need to study or achieve. For example, I give you samples of mnemonics, but I also teach you the more important thing: HOW to make mnemonics.

Often in the same class, all the students study almost the SAME materials, but there are some students that always manage to stay at the top of the class and get good grades on exams. Why? One very important factor is they have good study methods.

Hard work is important, but it needs to be combined with effective study methods. I think people need to work hard AND work SMART to be successful at their work, career, or anything else they are pursuing.

19. The importance of repetition: read this book <u>at least</u> three times

Repetition is one of the most important tips for learning. That is why I have listed it under a separate title. For example, you should treat this book as part of the core study materials for your ARE exams and you need to read this book <u>at least three times</u> to get all of its benefits:

1) The first time you read it, it is new information. You should focus on understanding and digesting the materials, and also do an <u>initial</u> review with the **3016** rule.
2) The second time you read it, focus on reading the parts <u>I</u> have already highlighted AND <u>you</u> have <u>highlighted</u> (the important parts and the weakest parts for you).
3) The third time, focus on <u>memorizing</u> the information.

Remember the analogy of the <u>memorization process</u> as **filling a cup with a hole on the bottom**?
Do NOT stop reading this book until you pass the real exam.

20. The importance of a routine

A routine is very important for studying. You should try to set up a routine that works for you. First, look at how much time you have to prepare for the exam, and then adjust your current routine to include exam preparation. Once you set up the routine, stick with it.

For example, you can spend from 8:00 a.m. to 12:00 noon, and 1:00 p.m. to 5:00 p.m. on studying new materials, and 7:00 p.m. to 10:00 p.m. to do an initial review of what you learned during the daytime. Then, switch your study content to mock exams, memorization and retention when it gets close to the exam date. This way, you have 11 hours for exam preparation everyday. You can probably pass an ARE exam in one week with this method. Just keep repeating it as a way to <u>retain</u> the architectural knowledge.

OR

You can spend 7:00 p.m. to 10:00 p.m. on studying new materials, and 6:00 a.m. to 7:00 a.m. to do an initial review of what you learned the evening before. This way, you have four hours for exam preparation every day. You can probably pass an ARE exam in two weeks with this preparation schedule.

A routine can help you to memorize important information because it makes it easier for you to concentrate and work with your body clock.

Do NOT become panicked and change your routine as the exam date gets closer. It will not help to change your routine and pull all-nighters right before the exam. In fact, if you pull an all-nighter the night before the exam, you may do much worse than you would have done if you kept your routine.

All-nighters or staying up late are not effective. For example, if you break your routine and stay up one-hour late, you will feel tired the next day. You may even have to sleep a few more hours the next day, adversely affecting your study regimen.

21. The importance of short, frequent breaks and physical exercise

Short, frequent breaks and physical exercise are VERY important for you, especially when you are spending a lot of time studying. They help relax your body and mind, making it much easier for you to concentrate when you study. They make you more efficient.

Take a five-minute break, such as a walk, at least once every one to two hours. Do at least 30 minutes of physical exercise every day.

If you feel tired and cannot concentrate, stop, go outside, and take a five-minute walk. You will feel much better when you come back.

You need your body and brain to work well to be effective with your studying. Take good care of them. You need them to be well-maintained and in excellent condition. You need to be able to count on them when you need them.

If you do not feel like studying, maybe you can start a little bit on your studies. Just casually read a few pages. Very soon, your body and mind will warm up and you will get into study mode.

Find a room where you will NOT be disturbed when you study. A good study environment is essential for concentration.

22. A strong vision and a clear goal

You need to have a strong vision and a clear goal: to master the architectural knowledge and become an architect in the shortest time. This is your number one priority. You need to master the architectural knowledge BEFORE you do sample questions or mock exams, except "truth-finding" exam or exercise at the very beginning of your exam prep. It will make the process much easier. Everything we discuss is to help you achieve this goal.

As I have mentioned on many occasions, and I say it one more time here because it is so important:

It is how much architectural knowledge and information you can understand, digest, memorize, and firmly retain that matters, not how many books you read or how many sample tests you have taken. The books and sample tests will NOT help you if you cannot understand, digest, memorize, and retain the important information for the ARE exam.

Cherish your limited time and effort and focus on the most important information.

23. English system (English or inch-pound units) vs. metric system (SI units)

This book is based on the English system or English units. The English or inch-pound units are based on the module used in the U.S. Effective July 2013, the ARE includes measurements in inch-pound units only. Metric system (SI units) is no longer used.

24. Codes and standards used in this book

We use the following codes and standards:

American Institute of Architects, Contract Documents, Washington, DC; ADA Standards for Accessible Design, ADA; Various International Codes by ICC. See Appendixes for more information.

25. Where can I find study materials on architectural history?

Every ARE exam may have a few questions related to architectural history. The following are some helpful links to FREE study materials on the topic:

http://issuu.com/motimar/docs/history_synopsis?viewMode=magazine

Chapter Two

Project Development & Documentation (PDD) Division

A. General Information

1. Exam content

The PDD division of the ARE has 120 items. Its exam content includes 5 sections:

Sections	Target Percentage	Expected Number of Items
Section 1: Integration of Building Materials & Systems	31-37%	37-45
Section 2: Construction Documentation	32-38%	38-46
Section 3: Project Manual & Specifications	12-18%	14-22
Section 4: Codes & Regulations	8-14%	9-17
Section 5: Construction Cost Estimates	2-8%	2-9

The exam content can be further broken down as follows:

Section 1: Integration of Building Materials & Systems (31-37%)
- Analyze the integration of architectural systems and technologies to meet project goals (A/E)
- Determine the size of mechanical, electrical, and plumbing systems and components to meet project goals (U/A)
- Determine the size of structural systems to meet project goals (U/A)
- Integrate specialty systems such as acoustics, lighting, fire suppression, conveying, security, and communications to meet project goals (U/A)
- Determine how to detail the integration of multiple building systems and technologies (U/A)
- Coordinate mechanical, electrical, plumbing, structural, and specialty systems and technologies (U/A)

Section 2: Construction Documentation (32-38%)
- Determine appropriate documentation of building design (A/E)
- Determine appropriate documentation of site features (A/E)
- Determine appropriate documentation of detailed building drawings within individual architectural systems (A/E)
- Apply standards required to assemble a set of clear and coordinated construction documentation (U/A)

- Determine impact of project changes on documentation requirements and methods to communicate those changes to owner and design team (U/A)
- Determine impact of project changes on documentation requirements and methods to communicate those changes to owner and design team (U/A)

Section 3: Project Manual & Specifications (12-18%)
- Identify and prioritize components required to write, maintain, and refine project manual (U/A)
- Identify and prioritize components required to write, maintain, and refine project specifications (U/A)
- Coordinate specifications with construction documentation (U/A)

Section 4: Codes & Regulations (8-14%)
- Determine adherence to building regulatory requirements (IBC) at detail level (U/A)
- Determine adherence with specialty regulatory requirements at the detail level (U/A)

Section 5: Construction Cost Estimates (2-8%)
- Analyze construction cost estimates to confirm alignment with project design (A/E)

2. Official exam guide and reference index for the Project Development & Documentation (PDD) division

NCARB published the exam guides for all ARE 5.0 division together as *ARE 5.0 Handbook*.

You need to read the official exam guide for the PDD division at least three times and become very familiar with it. The real exam is VERY similar to the sample questions in the handbook.

You can download the official *ARE 5.0 Handbook* at the following link:
http://blog.ncarb.org/2016/November/ARE5-Study-Materials.aspx

Note: We suggest you study the official ARE 5.0 Handbook first, and then other study materials, and then come back to Handbook again several days before the real ARE exam.

B. The Most Important Documents/Publications for PDD Division of the ARE Exam

1. Official NCARB list of formulas and references for the Project Development & Documentation (PDD) division with our comments and suggestions
You can find the NCARB list of references for the PPD division in the Appendixes of this book and the *ARE 5.0 Handbook*.

The formulas will be available during the real exam. You should read through them a few times before the exam to become familiar with the content. This will save you a lot of time during the real exam, and will help you solve structural calculations and other problems.

Note:
*While many of the MC questions in the real PDD ARE exam **focus on structural design concepts**, there are **some questions requiring calculations**. Therefore, it is absolutely necessary and critical for you to be very familiar with some of the basic and important equations, and to memorize them if possible. We have incorporated some of the most important equations into our PDD mock exam.*

In the ARE exams, it may be a good idea to skip any calculation question that requires over 30 seconds of your time; just pick a guess answer, mark it, and come back to calculate it at the end. This way, you have more time to read and answer other easier questions correctly.

A calculation question that takes 20 minutes to answer will gain the same number of points as a simple question that ONLY takes 2 minutes.

If you spend 20 minutes on a calculation question earlier, you risk losing the time to read and answer ten other easier questions, which could result in a loss of ten points instead of one.

The NCARB list of references includes the following:

Publications
Architectural Graphic Standards
The American Institute of Architects
John Wiley & Sons, latest edition

Building Codes Illustrated: A Guide to Understanding the 2012 International Building Code
Francis D.K. Ching and Steven R. Winkel, FAIA, PE
John Wiley & Sons, 2012

Building Structures
James Ambrose and Patrick Tripeny
John Wiley & Sons, 3rd edition, 2012

Fundamentals of Building Construction: Materials and Methods
Edward Allen and Joseph Iano
John Wiley & Sons, latest edition

Mechanical & Electrical Equipment for Buildings
Walter T. Grondzik, Alison G. Kwok, Benjamin Stein, and John S. Reynolds, Editors

John Wiley & Sons, latest edition

Codes
2010 ADA Standards for Accessible Design
U.S. Department of Justice, 2010

2012 International Building Code (IBC). International Code Council, Inc. Country Club Hills, Illinois, 2011

Focus on **Chapter 16**, particularly the sections on earthquakes and wind. Read them a few times, and have a general idea of the concepts. Do not force yourself to memorize all the details.

Read the following pages and become familiar with the Uniform and Concentrated Loads IBC table 1607.1:
pg. 285 & 286.
OR
You can read the Uniform and Concentrated Loads IBC Table 1607.1 for FREE at the following link:
http://publicecodes.cyberregs.com/icod/ibc/2006f2/icod_ibc_2006f2_16_sec001.htm

Note:
- *The latest version of IBC is the 2015 version. For your convenience, we provide a link to the free online version of the IBC. The basic IBC content stays the same for many years. If the codes are updated by NCARB in the future, you just need to go to the root directory and find the latest version of the codes:*
  http://codes.iccsafe.org

- *You need to spend a large percentage (at least 20%) of your prep time on IBC Chapter 16 and become familiar with it. You do not need to force yourself to memorize the numbers and all the detail. Just reading it a few times and becoming familiar with the information should be adequate.*

AIA Contract Documents
None of the standard list of AIA Contract Documents related to the ARE have specific content covered in the Project Development & Documentation (PDD) division.

The following are some extra study materials that are useful if you have some additional time and want to learn more. If you are tight on time, you can simply look through them and focus on the sections that cover your weaknesses:

2. *Manual of Steel Construction: Allowable Stress Design*; 9th Edition.
   American Institute of Steel Construction, Inc. Chicago, Illinois, 1989

Look through the following pages and become familiar with the structural shapes, designations, dimensions, and properties:
pg. 1-9 thru 1-16, *pg.* 1-18 thru 1-32, *pg.* 1-40 thru 1-41, *pg.* 1-46 thru 1-52, *pg.* 1-94 thru 1-103.

Make sure you understand what the designations stand for. For example, on pages 1-10 and 1-11, **W 40 x 298** means a W shape steel with a nominal depth of 40" (the actual depth is 39.69" per the Table on page 1-10), and a nominal weight of 298 lb. per ft. Use the diagram and Tables on pages 1-10 and 1-11 to look up the other detailed properties of a **W 40 x 298.** You do NOT need to remember any of these properties. You just need to know how to look them up and what they mean.

The most important information for an architect is the overall dimension of a structural member so that you can coordinate and make sure you have enough space to accommodate it. For example, you may need to find out if it will fit inside a wall or interstitial space.

You can also use the size of a structural member, the mechanical duct size, and the clearance space needed for a light fixture and/or fire sprinkler line to determine the interstitial height between floors.

Look through the following pages and become familiar with the beam nomenclature, diagrams, and formulas:
pg. 2-293 & 2-294, *pg.* 2-296, *pg.* 2-297, *pg.* 2-298, *pg.* 2-301, *pg.* 2-304, *pg.* 2-305.

Look through the following pages and become familiar with bolts, threaded parts, and rivet tensions:
pg. 4-3 & 4-5.

3. ***Steel Construction Manual***; 14th Edition. American Institute of Steel Construction, Inc. Chicago, Illinois, 2005
   Read and become familiar with the pages on the round HSS dimensions and properties:

4. **FREE information on truss and beam diagrams** can be found at the following link:
   http://ocw.mit.edu/ans7870/4/4.463/f04/module/Start.html

5. **The FREE PDF file of FEMA publication number 454 (FEMA454),** *Designing for Earthquakes: A Manual for Architects*, is available at the following link:
   http://www.fema.gov/library/viewRecord.do?id=2418

Note:
*You need to spend a large percentage (at least 30%) of your prep time on this **FEMA454** PDF file. Focus on **Chapters 4, 5, 8, and 9**. You may have **many real ARE questions** based on these chapters. This PDF book has many diagrams and photos and helps you understand what happened in buildings that failed during an earthquake.*

6. **The FREE PDF file of *Wind Design Made Simple*** by ICC TRI-Chapter Uniform Code Committee is available at the following link: http://www.calbo.org/Documents/SimplifiedWindHandout.pdf

   Note:
   You need to become familiar with this file. You do not need to force yourself to memorize the numbers and all the details, just reading it a few times and becoming familiar with the information should be adequate.

7. Arnold, Christopher. ***Building at Risk***, is available for FREE at the AIA website: http://www.aia.org/aiaucmp/groups/aia/documents/pdf/aiap016810.pdf

8. **Construction Specifications Institute (CSI) MasterFormat & *Building Construction***
   Become familiar with the new 6-digit CSI Construction Specifications Institute (CSI) MasterFormat as there may be a few questions based on this publication. Make sure you know which items/materials belong to which CSI MasterFormat specification section, and memorize the major section names and related numbers. For example, Division 9 is Finishes, and Division 5 is Metal, etc. Another one of my books, *Building Construction*, has detailed discussions on CSI MasterFormat specification sections.

   ### Mnemonics for the 2004 CSI MasterFormat

   The following is a good mnemonic, which relates to the 2004 CSI MasterFormat division names. Bold font signals the gaps in the numbering sequence.

   This tool can save you lots of time: if you can remember the four sentences below, you can easily memorize the order of the 2004 CSI MasterFormat divisions. The number sequencing is a bit more difficult, but can be mastered if you remember the five bold words and numbers that are not sequential. Memorizing this material will not only help you in several divisions of the ARE, but also in real architectural practice

   Mnemonics (pay attention to the underlined letters):
   Good students can memorize material when teachers order.
   F students earn F's simply 'cause **forgetting** principles have **an** effect. (21 and 25)
   C students **end** everyday understanding things without memorizing. (31)
   Please make professional pollution prevention inventions **everyday**. (40 and 48)

   1-Good................................. General Requirements
   2-Students............................. (Site) now Existing Conditions
   3-Can................................... Concrete
   4-Memorize........................... Masonry
   5-Material .... Metals
   6-When................................ Woods and Plastics
   7-Teachers............................ Thermal and Moisture
   8-Order................................ Openings

9-<u>F</u>..<u>F</u>inishes
10-<u>S</u>tudents............................ <u>S</u>pecialties
11-<u>E</u>arn.................................<u>E</u>quipment
12-<u>F</u>'s......................................<u>F</u>urnishings
13-<u>S</u>imply..............................<u>S</u>pecial Construction
14-'<u>C</u>ause...............................<u>C</u>onveying
21-<u>F</u>orgetting .... <u>F</u>ire
22-<u>P</u>rinciples.......................... <u>P</u>lumbing
23-<u>H</u>ave................................ <u>H</u>VAC
25-<u>A</u>n.................................... <u>A</u>utomation
26-<u>E</u>ffect.............................. <u>E</u>lectric

27-<u>C</u>...................................... <u>C</u>ommunication
28-<u>S</u>tudents............................ <u>S</u>afety & Security
31-<u>E</u>nd.................................... <u>E</u>arthwork
32-<u>E</u>veryday............................<u>E</u>xterior
33-<u>U</u>nderstanding ....<u>U</u>tilities
34-<u>T</u>hings...............................<u>T</u>ransportation
35-<u>W</u>ithout <u>M</u>emorizing........ <u>W</u>aterways and <u>M</u>arine

40-<u>P</u>lease...............................<u>P</u>rocess Integration
41-<u>M</u>ake................................ <u>M</u>aterial Processing and Handling Equipment
42-<u>P</u>rofessional...................... <u>P</u>rocess Heating, Cooling, and Drying Equipment
43-<u>P</u>ollution........................... <u>P</u>rocess Gas and Liquid Handling, Purification and Storage Equipment
44-<u>P</u>revention........................<u>P</u>ollution Control Equipment
45-<u>I</u>nventions........................ <u>I</u>ndustry-Specific Manufacturing Equipment
48-<u>E</u>veryday...........................<u>E</u>lectrical Power Generation

Note:
There are 49 CSI divisions. The "missing" divisions are those "reserved for future expansion" by CSI. They are intentionally omitted from the list.

Chapter Three

ARE Mock Exam for
Project Development & Documentation (PDD) Division

A. **Multiple-Choice (MC)**

1. Which of the following should be specified to affix shingles onto roof structure? **Check the two that apply.**
   a. Stainless steel nails
   b. Iron nails
   c. Staplers using pneumatic staple guns
   d. Terne-coated stainless steel

2. Which of the following has been banned in new construction? **Check the two that apply.**
   a. Copper nails
   b. Lead-based paint
   c. Zinc-based paint
   d. Asbestos

3. Which of the following should not have direct contact with copper nails?
   a. 4-ply roofing
   b. Fiber-glass roofing
   c. Red-cedar shingles
   d. TPO roofing

4. Which of the following statements is incorrect? **Check the two that apply.**
   a. Construction joints also serve as isolation or control joints.
   b. Control joints also serve as isolation or construction joints.
   c. Construction joints normally run from the top of slab to the bottom of the slab.
   d. Control joints normally run from the top of slab to the bottom of the slab.

5. The term "fine sand float finish" refers to
   a. plastering
   b. paving
   c. painting
   d. concrete

6. The term "VOC" refers to
   a. Valid Organic Compound
   b. Volatile Organic Compound
   c. Volatile Original Compound

    d. Volatile Original Composite

7. Which of the following is the most cost-effective finish for exterior walls?
    a. Full-brick veneer
    b. Thin-brick veneer
    c. Stone veneer
    d. Plastering

8. According to *International Building Code* (IBC), which of the following statement is true at stairways where handrails are not continuous between flights?
    a. The handrails shall extend at least 12" (305) beyond the top riser and continue to slope for the depth of one tread beyond the bottom riser.
    b. The handrails shall extend at least 12" (305) beyond the top riser and continue to slope for the depth of one tread plus 12" (305) beyond the bottom riser.
    c. The handrails shall extend at least 12" (305) plus the depth of one tread beyond the top riser and extend at least 12" (305) beyond the bottom riser.
    d. The handrails shall extend at least 12" (305) beyond the top riser and extend at least 12" (305) beyond the bottom riser.

9. According to *International Building Code* (IBC), stair riser heights shall be _____ maximum and _____ minimum. Rectangular stair tread depths shall be _____ minimum.

10. The term "Elastomeric - Modified Acrylic" is most likely to be found in the specifications for
    a. plastering
    b. paving
    c. painting
    d. concrete

11. An architect is drawing the roof plan. There is a chimney penetrating the roof at the central area of the roof. She is trying to drain the rainwater away from the Chimney. Which of the following is true?
    a. She should add gabled flashings on the high side of the roof, next to the chimney, to drain rainwater.
    b. She should add gabled flashings on the low side of the roof, next to the chimney, to drain rainwater.
    c. She should add a cricket on the high side of the roof, next to the chimney, to drain rainwater.
    d. She should add a cricket on the low side of the roof, next to the chimney, to drain rainwater.

12. Which of the following is the best about travel distance? **Check the two that apply.**
    a. A travel distance is measured from the door of the most remote room, within a story.
    b. A travel distance is measured from the most remote point, within a story.

c. When the path of exit access includes unenclosed stairway, the distance of travel on the stair shall be included in the travel distance measurement.

d. When the path of exit access includes unenclosed stairway, the distance of travel on the stair shall not be included in the travel distance measurement.

13. An architect is preparing the plan check package for a retail store. Which of the following statements are true? **Check the two that apply.**

a. If the store sells fresh produce and meat, the architect probably needs to submit the plans to Health Department for plan check.

b. If the store sells clothing, the architect probably needs to submit the plans to Health Department for plan check.

c. If the store sells candies, the architect probably needs to submit the plans to Health Department for plan check.

d. If the store sells candies, the architect probably does not need to submit the plans to Health Department for plan check.

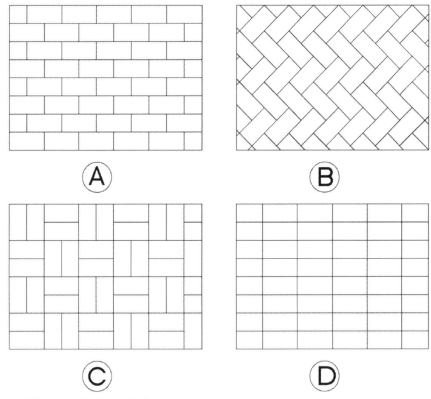

Figure 3.1   Brick pattern

14. Which pattern/letter on the previous image is likely to have the highest construction cost?

a. Pattern A

b. Pattern B

c. Pattern C

d. Pattern D

15. What is the purpose of the weep holes at the bottom of the CMU retaining walls?
    a. To vent the air from the bottom of the retaining wall
    b. To let small insects pass through the retaining walls to preserve biodiversity
    c. To drain water from the bottom of the retaining wall
    d. To provide room for the expansion of CMU

16. Which of the following statements are true? **Check the two that apply.**
    a. Single-glass windows typically have a higher R-value than double-glass windows.
    b. Single-glass windows typically have a lower R-value than double-glass windows.
    c. Single-glass windows typically have a higher U-value than double-glass windows
    d. Single-glass windows typically have a lower U-value than double-glass windows

17. For hydraulic elevators, the depth of the piston cylinder well is:
    a. equal to 1/2 the height of elevator travel
    b. equal to 1/3 the height of elevator travel
    c. equal to the height of elevator travel
    d. equal to twice the height of elevator travel

18. A client selects a site with underground methane gas to build a supermarket. Which of the following statements are true? **Check the two that apply.**
    a. The contractor should use special construction techniques to avoid explosion at the site.
    b. The contractor should have his employee use special masks at the site.
    c. The contractor can use underground-perforated pipes to collect the methane gas.
    d. The contractor can use automatic vent damper devices to alleviate the methane gas problem

19. Where should the vapor barrier be installed?
    a. On the inside of the wall insulation
    b. On the outside of the wall insulation
    c. On the warm side of the walls
    d. On the cold side of the walls

20. Architects often specify Type "X" Gypsum Wallboard for
    a. Low cost
    b. Recyclability
    c. Ease of installation
    d. Fire resistance

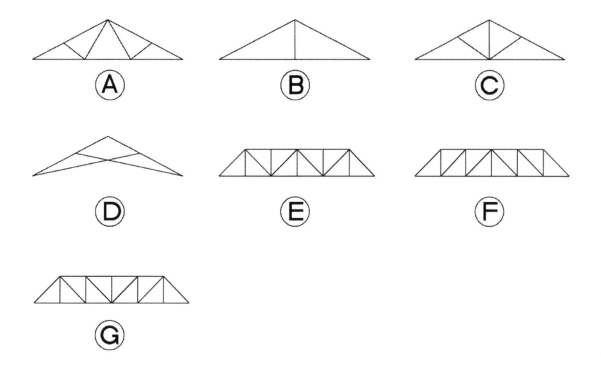

Figure 3.2   Truss types

21. Which of the previous images shows a fink truss?
    a. A
    b. B
    c. C
    d. D
    e. E
    f. F
    g. G

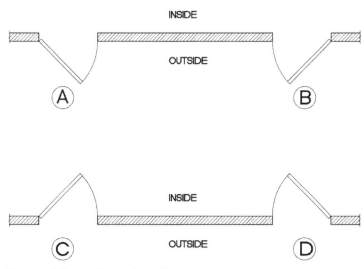

Figure 3.3   Door handing

22. Which of the previous images shows a right-hand door?
    a. A
    b. B
    c. C
    d. D

23. If some of the exposed beams of an historic building have deflection, which of the following is recommended? **Check the two that apply.**
    a. Leaving them in place without doing anything
    b. Augmenting or upgrading
    c. Protecting and maintaining the beams and ensuring that structural members are free from insect infestation.
    d. Replacement of all the beams

24. Which of the following is not recommended when working on the preservation of the interior of a historic building? **Check the two that apply.**
    a. Installing protective coverings for wall coverings in the corridors
    b. Replacement of broken window glazing
    c. Using propane to remove paint
    d. Sandblasting of character-defining features

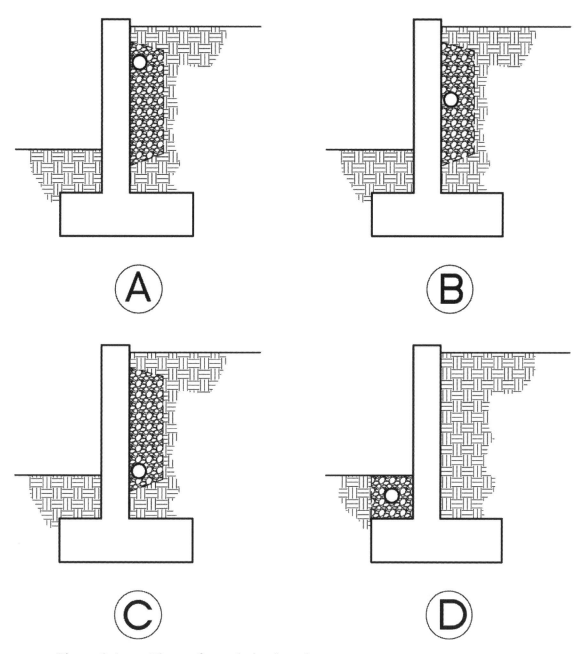

Figure 3.4   The perforated pipe location

25. Which of the previous images shows the correct location of a perforated pipe?
    a. A
    b. B
    c. C
    d. D

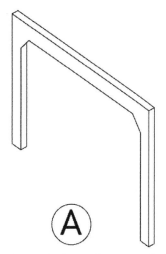

Figure 3.5   Structural element

26. Which structural element does the previous image show?
    a. Column and beam
    b. Rigid frame
    c. Space frame
    d. Prefabricated column and beam

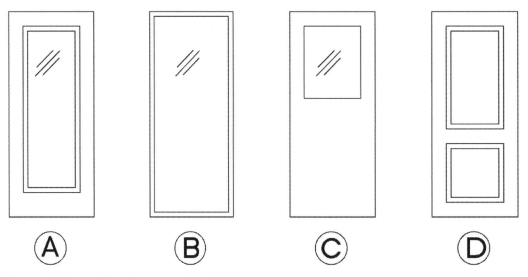

Figure 3.6   The door types by design

27. Which of the previous images shows a "Sash" type door design?
    a. A
    b. B
    c. C
    d. D

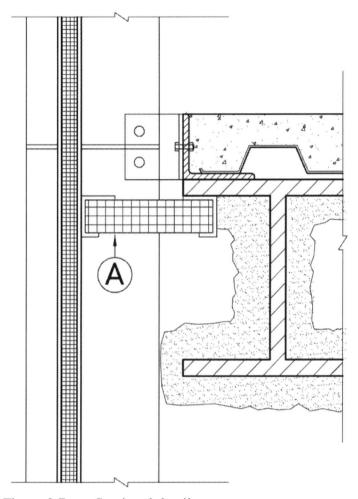

Figure 3.7   Sectional detail

28. Which of the following is the correct term for A in previous image?
    a. Beam plate
    b. Sliptrack
    c. Firestopping
    d. Steel support

29. In a fast track, one-story project, which of the following is most likely a critical path item?
    a. Roof framing system design
    b. HVAC system design
    c. Interior finish selection
    d. Door selection

30. Which of the following situations shall utilize grade beams? **Check the two that apply.**
    a. At site with expansive soils
    b. At storefront with no solid walls
    c. At site with underground rock
    d. At site in an inland area

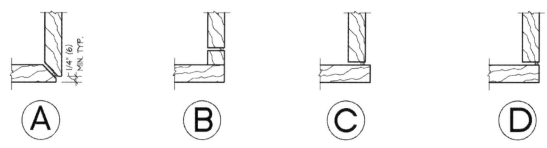

Figure 3.8   Veneer stone corner joints

31. Which of the following is the correct term for previous image A?
    a. Corner "L"
    b. Quirk miter
    c. Slip corner
    d. Butt joint

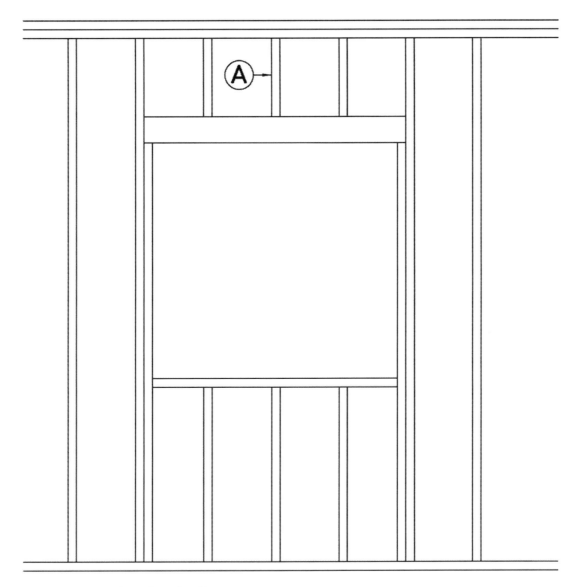

Figure 3.9   Framing detail

32. Which of the following is the correct term for A in previous image?
    a. Cripple studs
    b. King posts
    c. Transom studs
    d. Top studs

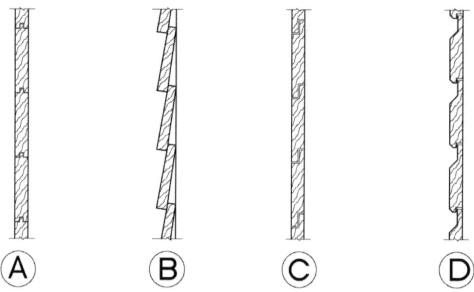

Figure 3.10   Wood siding

33. Which of the following is the correct term for the wood siding A in previous image?
    a. Bevel
    b. Shiplap
    c. Square edge tongue and groove
    d. Channel rustic

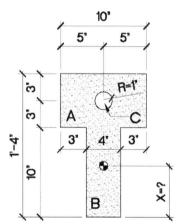

Figure 3.11   Locate the centroid of the hatched area

34. Locate the centroid of the hatched area as shown in figure 3.11 and calculate to find that x = _____.

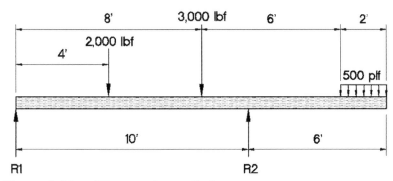

Figure 3.12   The reactions of a beam

35. The reactions of the beam shown in figure 3.12 are
    a. R_1 = 1,200 lbf, R_2 = 4,600 lbf
    b. R_1 = 4,600 lbf, R_2 = 1,200 lbf
    c. R_1 = 1,300 lbf, R_2 = 4,700 lbf
    d. R_1 = 4,700 lbf, R_2 = 1,300 lbf

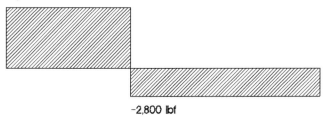

Figure 3.13   What is this diagram?

36. Figure 3.13 shows
    a.   a shear diagram of uniformly distributed loads
    b.   a shear diagram of concentrated loads
    c.   a load diagram
    d.   none of the above

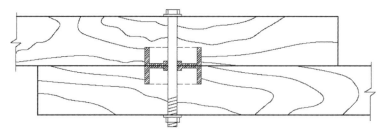

Figure 3.14   What does this diagram show?

37. Figure 3.14 shows a
    a. split ring connector
    b. shear plate connector
    c. double shear connector
    d. multiple shear connector

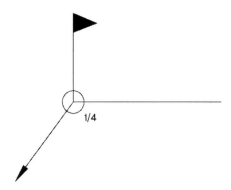

Figure 3.15   What does this diagram show?

38. Figure 3.15 shows a
    a. field weld
    b. flare weld
    c. bevel weld
    d. square weld

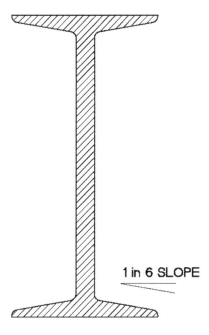

Figure 3.16   What does this diagram show?

39. The structural steel shown in figure 3.16 is a
    a. "C" shape
    b. "ST" shape
    c. "S" shape
    d. "W" shape
    a.

Figure 3.17   A simply supported beam

40. The section A-A of a simply supported beam shown in figure 3.17 has (**Check the two that apply.**)
    a. tension stresses in the top half of the beam
    b. compression stresses in the top half of the beam
    c. tension stresses in the bottom half of the beam
    d. compression stresses in the bottom half of the beam

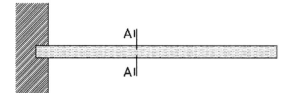

Figure 3.18   A cantilever beam

41. Section A-A of the cantilever beam shown in figure 3.18 has (**Check the two that apply.**)
    a. tension stresses in the top half of the beam
    b. compression stresses in the top half of the beam
    c. tension stresses in the bottom half of the beam
    d. compression stresses in the bottom half of the beam

42. What is the total horizontal load exerted on a 4-foot-high retaining wall? The wall is retaining inorganic silts and clayey silts with an active pressure of 45 psf/ft.
    a. 240 psf
    b. 360 psf
    c. 480 psf
    d. 600 psf

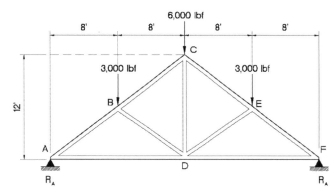

Figure 3.19   A simple truss

43. Figure 3.19 shows a simple truss. Using the method of sections, the force in member BC is
    a. A
    b. B
    c. C
    d. E

Figure 3.20   A structural item

44. Figure 3.20 shows a (an)
    a. lag screw
    b. anchor bolt
    c. hold-down bolt
    d. base plate screw

Figure 3.21   A structural item

45. Figure 3.21 shows a (an)
    a. lag screw
    b. anchor bolt

      c. hold-down bolt

      d. base plate screw

46. _____ are used to reduce the amount of water needed for mixing concrete.
      a. Accelerators
      b. Air-entraining agents
      c. Plasticizers
      d. Fine aggregates

Figure 3.22   A structural item

47. Figure 3.22 shows a
      a. column base
      b. strap
      c. hold-down
      d. structural plate

48. Which of the following are two different designations for the same welded wire fabric? **Select the two that apply.**
      a. 6x6-10/10
      b. 6x6-W1.0x1.0
      c. 6x6-W1.2x1.2
      d. 6x6-W1.4x1.4
      e. 6x6-W1.6x1.6

49. Which of the following diagrams in figure 3.23 show correct placement of rebar for the concrete beams of a gas station canopy supported by concrete columns? (Some elements are not shown for clarity.)
    a. A
    b. B
    c. C
    d. D

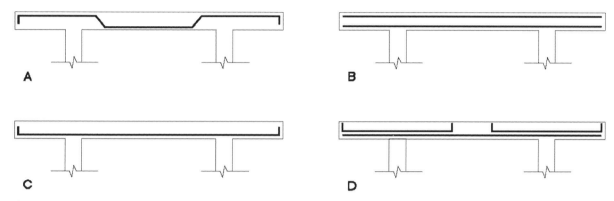

Figure 3.23   Rebar for beams at a concrete canopy

50. Using Method II, which of the following diagrams in figure 3.24 show the correct direction of wind pressure?
    a. A
    b. B
    c. C
    d. D

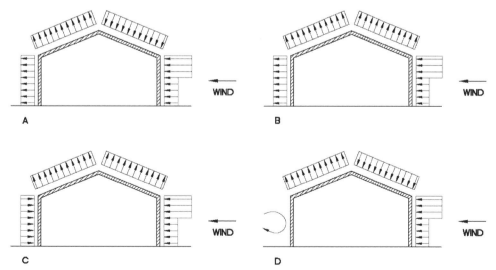

Figure 3.24   Direction of wind loads

51. Which of the following diaphragms in figure 3.25 is a correct diagram of wind loads?
    a. A
    b. B
    c. C
    d. D

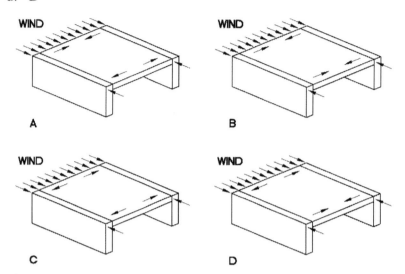

Figure 3.25   Wind loads acting on a diaphragm

52. In reference to figure 3.26, the brace at location A is in
    a. tension
    b. compression
    c. tension on top and compression at the bottom
    d. none of the above

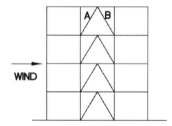

Figure 3.26   K-brace

53. Site Class A, B, C, D, E, or F in Chapter 16 of IBC is based on
    a. earthquake zones
    b. wind load zones
    c. soil properties
    d. none of the above

54. For a hospital, the Importance Factor (I Factor) for snow is:
    a. 1.15
    b. 1.2
    c. 1.25
    d. 1.5

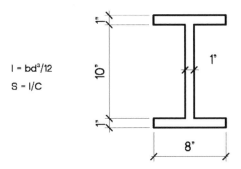

Figure 3.27   Section modulus

55. The section modulus for the geometric section as shown in figure 3.27 is_____
    _____in^3.

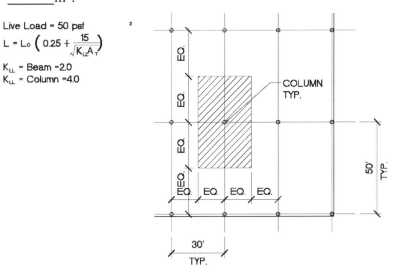

Figure 3.28   The live load for the floor supported by a column

56. The live load for the floor supported by the column as shown in figure 3.28 is
    _____kips (kg).

57. The tendency of a solid material to move slowly or deform permanently under the influence
    of sustained stress is called
    a. shrinkage
    b. temperature expansion
    c. creep
    d. contraction

58. When the ratio of a slab's length (long direction to short direction) is greater than _____it
    can be considered a one-way slab.
    a. 3:2
    b. 2:1
    c. 5:2
    d. 3:1

59. Which of the following in figure 3.29 is an eccentrically braced frame (EBF)?

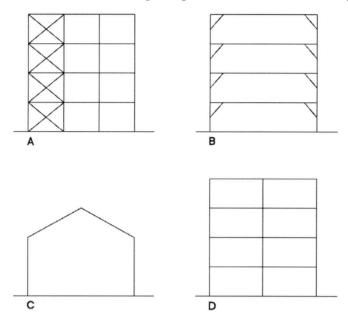

Figure 3.29   Pick an eccentrically braced frame (EBF)

60. For the flexible diaphragm shown in figure 3.30, what is the shear at F_2?
    a. 15 kips
    b. 20 kips
    c. 25 kips
    d. 30 kips

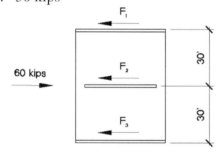

Figure 3.30   A flexible diaphragm

61. If resisted only by gravity forces, what is the factor of safety against overturning for a concrete shear wall as shown in figure 3.31? Suppose the weight of concrete equals 150 lb/ft³ [23.5 kN/m3], and the dead load equals 300 kips [1325 kN].
Disregard the weight of the soil over the footing.
    a. 5.91
    b. 6.91
    c. 7.91
    d. 8.91

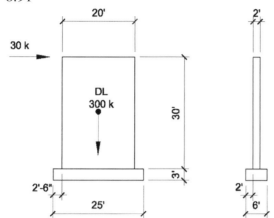

Figure 3.31   The factor of safety against overturning for a concrete shear wall

62. Which of the following is a method used to determine wind loads on a structure? **Check the two that apply.**
    a. normal force method
    b. lateral force method
    c. projected area method
    d. diagram method

63. Which of the following statements regarding earthquakes is true? **Check the two that apply.**
    a. P wave is a wave that moves perpendicular to the ground surface.
    b. P wave is a primary wave that alternately pushes (compresses) and pulls (dilates) the rock.
    c. P waves, just like acoustic waves, are able to travel through solid rock, such as granite and alluvium; through soils; and through liquids, such as volcanic magma or the water of lakes and oceans.
    d. S waves, just like acoustic waves, are able to travel through solid rock, such as granite and alluvium; through soils; and through liquids, (such as volcanic magma or the water of lakes and oceans.

64. The three basic alternative types of vertical lateral force–resisting systems are _____
_____.

65. Inland waterways belong to which wind exposure category per ASCE 7?
   a. Exposure A
   b. Exposure B
   c. Exposure C
   d. Exposure D

66. Figure 3.32 shows a reinforced concrete wall. Which of the following statements is correct?
   a. Pier 1 and Pier 2 resist more lateral load than Pier 3 and Pier 4.
   b. Pier 1 and Pier 3 resist more lateral load than Pier 2 and Pier 4.
   c. Pier 1 and Pier 4 resist more lateral load than Pier 2 and Pier 3.
   d. Pier 3 and Pier 4 resist more lateral load than Pier 1 and Pier 2.
   e. Each pier resists the same lateral load.

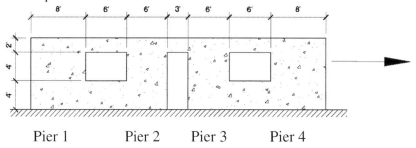

Figure 3.32   Distribution of lateral load for a reinforced concrete wall

67. Figure 3.33 shows a 2-story room addition to a 1-story existing building. Which of the following statements is correct?
   a. Column A will resist more lateral load than the other columns.
   b. Column B will resist more lateral load than the other columns.
   c. Column C will resist more lateral load than the other columns.
   d. Column D will resist more lateral load than the other columns.
   e. Each column resists the same lateral load.

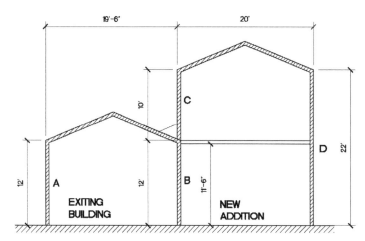

Figure 3.33   Which column will resist more lateral load than the other columns?

68. Figure 3.34 shows a 3-story moment-resisting frame with hinged bases resisting lateral loads. Ignoring the dead loads, what force resists the overturning caused by the lateral loads?
    a. shear in the columns
    b. moment at the column bases
    c. tension in one hinge base, and compression in another hinge base
    d. tension in the beams
    e. compression in the beams

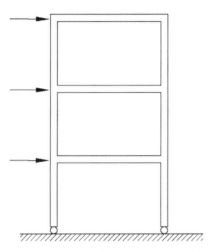

Figure 3.34   Moment-resisting frame with hinged bases

69. Referring to the same 3-story moment-resisting frame as shown in figure 3.34, if we include the dead load, what resists the overturning caused by the lateral loads? **Check the two that apply.**
    a. shear in the columns
    b. weight of the columns
    c. moment at the column bases
    d. tension in one hinge base, and compression in another hinge base
    e. tension in the beams
    f. weight of a column and beams
    g. compression in the beams
    h. tension or compression in one hinge base, and compression in another hinge base

70. Which of the diagrams in figure 3.35 show the deflected shape of a rigid frame with a rigid base for the loading shown?

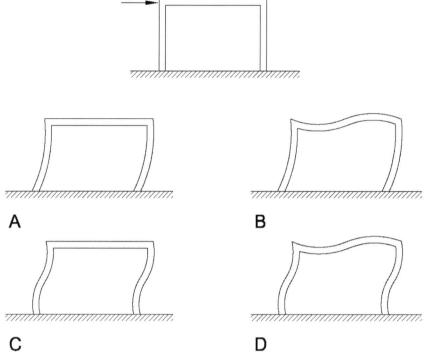

Figure 3.35   Diagram for a rigid frame

71. A horizontal force of 25 kips is applied to a frame with diagonal braces made of cables as shown in figure 3.36. What is the internal tension in each brace?
    a.   brace 1 = 0, brace 2 = 35.36 kips
    b.   brace 1 = 0, brace 2 = 25 kips
    c.   brace 1 = 35.36, brace 2 = 0 kips
    d.   brace 1 = 25, brace 2 = 0 kips

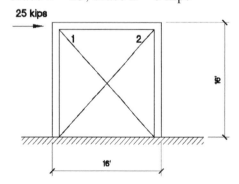

Figure 3.36   Diagram for a frame

72. Which of the systems shown in figure 3.37 is stable under lateral forces? **Check the two that apply.**

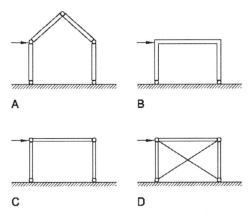

Figure 3.37   Diagram for seismic forces

73. Figure 3.38 shows a shear wall with 500 lb of dead load on each end, and 500 lb of lateral load. What is the net uplift at point 1?
    a.   10,000 lb
    b.   5,000 lb
    c.   2,500 lb
    d.   zero

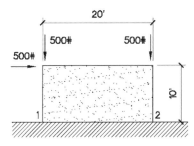

Figure 3.38   A shear wall

74. You are designing a sewer line. The city requires a minimum slope of 1/4" per foot (2.08%) for sewer lines. If the sewer line has to run a horizontal distance of 90 feet (27.43m), the minimum vertical rise has to be_____ feet.

75. The transfer of heat from one place to another by the movement of fluids is called
    a.   convection
    b.   radiation
    c.   conduction
    d.   mass transfer

76. Which of the following are ways for the human body to lose heat? **Check the four that apply.**
    a. ventilation
    b. evaporation
    c. conduction
    d. convection
    e. radiation
    condensation

77. _____is a pressure surge that can occur when water is shut off or forced to change direction abruptly.

78. Which of the following statements are true? **Check the two that apply.**
    a. Both the roof drains and over flow drains should be connected to a storm drain if possible.
    b. Roof drains should be connected to a storm drain if possible.
    c. A floor drain can be connected to a sewer line.
    d. A grease interceptor can be connected to a sewer line.

79. A pipe with a maximum of_____inch outside diameter can fit inside a 6" wood stud wall.

80. A 2" copper pipe means
    a. the inner diameter of the pipe is 2"
    b. the outside diameter of the pipe is 2"
    c. the inner diameter of the pipe is a little larger than 2"
    d. the inner diameter of the pipe is a little smaller than 2"

81. For a faucet in a house, what type of valve is most likely used?
    a. gate valve
    b. globe valve
    c. check valve
    d. angle valve

82. Which of the following power supplies is common for residences?
    a. 120/240 V, single-phase, three-wire system
    b. 120/208 V, three-phase, four-wire system
    c. 277/480 V, three-phase, four-wire system
    d. 2400/4160 V, three-phase, four-wire system

83. Which of the following fixture types are permitted to connect to a soil stack vent? **Check the two that apply.**
    a. bidets
    b. urinals
    c. lavatories
    d. toilets

84. What is the minimum height of a handicapped accessible receptacle outlet above the floor?
    a. 6"
    b. 12"
    c. 15"
    d. 18"

85. Which piping material has the lowest coefficient of thermal expansion?
    a. PVC
    b. copper
    c. iron
    d. glass

86. Which of the following statements regarding fixture installation and the transfer of luminaire's heat are incorrect? **Check the two that apply.**
    a. Suspended fixtures transfer all their heat to the space, and they remain cool.
    b. Surfaced-mounted fixtures transfer all their heat to the space, and they remain cool.
    c. Surfaced-mounted fixtures transfer about 50% their heat to the space, and they run hot.
    d. Completely recessed and enclosed fixtures transfer about 50% of their heat to the plenum.
    e. Baffled or open louvered fixtures transfer about 75% of their heat to the plenum.

87. An architect needs to calculate the U-value (overall thermal transmittance) for a wall assembly. Based on the following data, what is the U-value for the wall?

Component	R-value
Outside air layer	0.17
3/4" Cement plaster, sand aggregate	0.15
½" Plywood	0.62
Nominal 3" batt fiberglass	11.00
Gypsum board	0.45
Inside air layer	0.68

    a. approximately 0.02
    b. approximately 0.05
    c. approximately 0.08
    d. approximately 0.10

88. An architect is designing a classroom. The optimum reverberation time is 0.35 seconds and, the classroom is 22'-0" wide, 20'-0" long, and 12'-0" high. What should the total room absorption be to achieve optimum reverberation time?
    a. approximately 250 sabins
    b. approximately 500 sabins
    c. approximately 750 sabins
    d. approximately 1000 sabins

89. A normal human being can hear sound in the range of
    a. 20 Hz to 2,000 Hz
    b. 20 Hz to 20,000 Hz
    c. 200 Hz to 20,000 Hz
    d. 200 Hz to 30,000 Hz

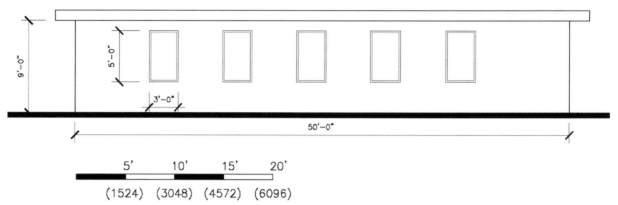

Figure 3.39   South elevation of a building

90. For the south elevation shown in figure 3.39, if the U-value for the windows is 0.35, and overall U-value for the entire south wall is 0.086, what is the R-value for the opaque wall?
    a. approximately 13
    b. approximately 19
    c. approximately 30
    d. approximately 35

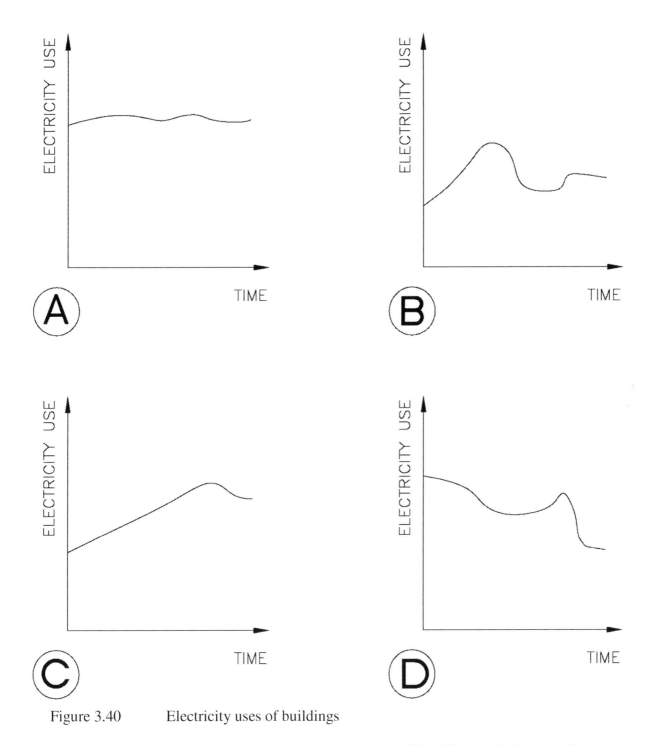

Figure 3.40   Electricity uses of buildings

91. Figure 3.40 shows the energy use of four "all-electrical" buildings with the same floor area and location at 32 degrees north of the Equator. Which building will benefit the most from seeking LEED certification?
   a. A
   b. B
   c. C
   d. D

92. An architect needs to set the spot elevations at the perimeter of a one-story supermarket building. If the finish floor elevation is 112.00', what is a proper spot elevation at the front entrance if the front door has a threshold?
    a. 111.75'
    b. 111.96'
    c. 112.00'
    d. 112.25'

93. For the same one-story supermarket building in previous question, what is a proper spot elevation at the front entrance if the front door has no threshold?
    a. 111.75'
    b. 111.98'
    c. 112.00'
    d. 112.25'

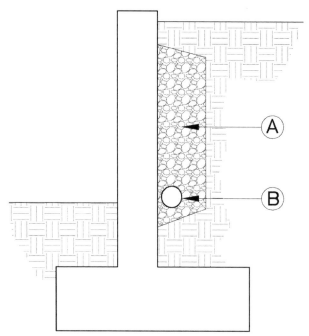

Figure 3.41   Retaining wall section

94. Which of the following is B as shown on Figure 3.41?
    a. Sewer line
    b. Storm drain
    c. Perforated pipe
    d. Water line

95. Which of the following are acceptable ways to revise drawings and specifications during construction? **Check the three that apply.**
    a. Addenda
    b. Notices
    c. Change orders
    d. Written orders for a minor change of the Work
    e. Construction Change directives
    f. Punch lists

96. Which of the following can affect a project's construction cost?
    I. Project location
    II. Schedule
    III. Type of construction
    IV. LEED certification

    a. I and II
    b. II and III
    c. I, II, and III
    d. All of the above

97. Which of the following is correct?
    a. An architect shall assist the owner and issue modifications to contractors during bidding process.
    b. An architect just needs to prepare one estimate of the construction cost to the owner.
    c. If an architect just needs to prepare estimate of the construction cost to the owner, she should treat this as an additional service.
    d. An architect shall obtain the owner's approval before proceeding to the next phase of design.

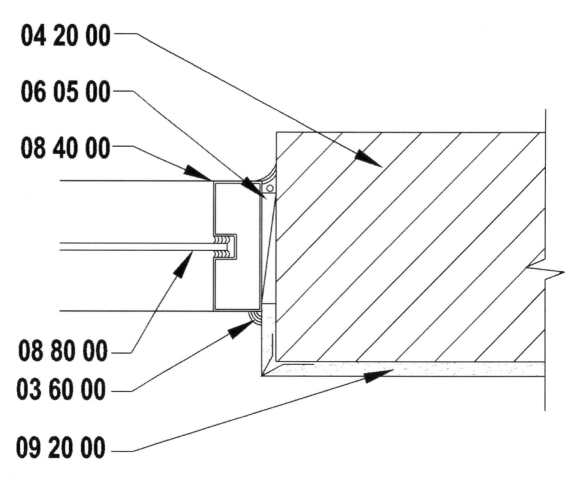

Figure 3.42   Numbered keynotes

98. The numbered keynotes above refer to the
    a. product codes
    b. building code sections
    c. specification sections
    d. finish schedule codes

99. During the construction phase, which of the following are the architect's responsibilities? **Check the three that apply.**
    a. Review every submittal submitted by the contractor
    b. Issue changes requested by the owner
    c. Issues Addenda
    d. Field observations
    e. Issue Construction Change Directives
    f. Prepares the Punch List

100. Which of the following are contract documents according to A201–2007, General Conditions of the Contract for Construction? **Check the three that apply.**
    a. Invitation to bid
    b. Instruction to Bidders
    c. Supplementary Condition
    d. Contractor's proposal
    e. Drawings and Specifications
    f. Construction Change Directive

101. Which of the following are more likely to be an architect's instrument of service? **Check the four that apply.**
    a. Civil plans
    b. Geotechnical studies
    c. Project research and studies
    d. Drawings and specifications by architect
    e. Sketches
    f. Electrical single line diagram

102. A project has a liquated damage cause. Because of the delay of the shipment of an electrical switchgear, the final completion is 1 month behind schedule. Who should pay the owner for monetary damages?
    a. The electrical subcontractor
    b. The contractor
    c. The supplier of the electrical switchgear
    d. The contractor should pay for most of the damages, and the electrical subcontractor should pay a portion of it.

103. An architect incorporates some specific construction methods into the construction documents per the owner's prototype plans. The contractor reviews the plans and notice the specific construction methods in the plans are not safe. He immediately calls both the owner and the architect to notify them about his concerns. The owner instructs the contractor to proceed as the original construction documents. A worker is injured while performing the work as per the construction methods in the original construction documents. Who should be responsible for this construction accident?
    a. The owner
    b. The contractor
    c. The owner and the contractor
    d. The owner and the architect

104. The contract documents call for 32 sets of door hardware. The contractor's submittal shows 30 sets of door hardware and is accidentally approved by the architect. The contractor later submits a claim for the extra cost for 2 sets of door hardware citing the submittal approved by the architect. What should the architect do?
    a. Negotiate with the contractor and split the extra cost of the 2 sets of door hardware.
    b. Reject the contractor's claim for the extra cost for 2 sets of door hardware.
    c. Submit a claim to the architect's error and omission insurance carrier for the extra cost for 2 sets of door hardware.
    d. Issue a change order to increase the contract sum to cover the 2 sets of door hardware.

105. At a field visit, the architect notices a subcontractor standing on a foam cornice next to the parapet. She is concerned about the safety procedures at the site. What should she do?
    a. Instruct the subcontractor not to stand on the foam cornice since it may not be strong enough to support a human weight.
    b. Do nothing, since jobsite safety procedures are the contractor's sole responsibility.
    c. Notify the owner about her concerns.
    d. Notify the superintendent about her concerns.

106. The contractor unbound the plans and gave specific sections to subcontractors for bidding. The contractor later found out there are gaps in the over coverage of the bid. Which of the following statements is true?
    a. The subcontractors should split and absorb the cost of the work.
    b. The contractor should absorb the cost of the work.
    c. The owner should pay for the work because she has not paid for it in the original bid.
    d. The architect should revise supplementary condition to cover the work.

107. The contractor decided not to purchase the roof tiles at the beginning of a project because they would not be needed until months later. When he purchased the roof tiles, the price of roof tiles has risen 50% because of the damages caused by Hurricane Katrina. Which of the following is true?
    a. The contractor is not entitled to a change order.
    b. The architect should issue a change order to cover the extra cost because the damages caused by Hurricane Katrina could not be anticipated.
    c. The owner's insurance company should pay for the extra cost.
    d. The owner should pay for the extra cost.

108. A contract executed on January 3, 2009 required the contractor to start the Work on January 15, 2009. The contract time is 180 days. The contractor started the Work on February 1. Substantial completion occurred on July 8, 2009. Final completion occurred on August 6, 2009. Had the contractor finished the project within the time required by the contract?
    a. No, the contractor had not finished the project within the contract time because the final completion occurred over 180 days after the commencement of the work (January 15, 2009).
    b. No, the contractor had not finished the project within the contract time because the final completion occurred over 180 days after the commencement of the work (February 1, 2009).
    c. Yes, the contractor had finished the project within the contract time because the substantial completion occurred within 180 days of the commencement of the work (January 15, 2009).
    d. Yes, the contractor had finished the project within the contract time because the substantial completion occurred within 180 days of the commencement of the work (February 1, 2009).

109. If a contractor fails to pay one of his subcontractors, the owner can issue a _____ check to the contractor and to the subcontractor who has not been paid by the contractor.

110. If asbestos or PCB is discovered at the concealed space of a project, which of the following is true? **Check the three that apply.**
    a. The contractor should stop the Work immediately.
    b. The contractor should stop the work at the affected area immediately.
    c. The contractor is entitled to a change order.
    d. The contractor is not entitled to a change order.
    e. If the contractor and the owner cannot reach an agreement regarding the asbestos issue, the contractor should submit a claim to the architect for initial determination.
    f. If the contractor and the owner cannot reach an agreement regarding the asbestos issue, the contractor should proceed to mediation.

B. Case Study

Questions 111 through 120 refer to the following case study. See figure 3.43 though figure 3.45 for information necessary to answer the questions.

You are designing an office building, and need to design a roof plan per the following requirements:

1) The building has two volumes, one low and one high. Each volume has its own roof height and slope requirements (figure 3.43).
2) The site is in a temperate climate, and has moderate annual rainfall.
3) You can only use roof slope, downspout, and roof gutter to remove rainwater.
4) Downspouts shall not conflict with any window, clerestory window, or door.
5) Rainwater shall not discharge from any gutter or roof directly onto the ground, or from the edge of an upper roof directly onto a lower roof.
6) Finish floor elevation is 0'-0". Minimum ceiling height is 8'-0".
7) All roof areas shall have positive drainage.
8) The slope for the Multi-Purpose Room should be between 6:12 and 12:12.
   - The total thickness for the roof and structural assembly is 18".
9) The slope for the remaining spaces should be between 2:12 and 5:12.
   - The total thickness for the roof and structural assembly is 18".
10) The Multi-Purpose Room has a 30-inch-high continuous horizontal clerestory window in the existing east wall.
    - The clerestory sill is included in the overall height dimension.
11) All rooms shall have natural light from a skylight, window, or clerestory window.
    - You can only use skylights for rooms without a window, or clerestory window.
    - Storage rooms, closets, and halls do NOT require skylights.
12) You need to show flashing for all roof and wall surface intersections, including chimneys.
13) Gutters, skylights, exhaust fan vents, plumbing vent stacks, and HVAC condensing units are self-flashing, and do not require additional crickets or flashing.
14) You need to place the HVAC condensing unit on a roof with a slope of 5:12 or less.
    - Do not place in front of the clerestory window.
    - Maintain a minimum of 3'-0" clearance from all roof edges.
15) Provide one exhaust fan for each toilet room.
16) Provide one exhaust fan for the kitchen.
17) Provide vent stacks through the roof where required to vent plumbing fixtures.

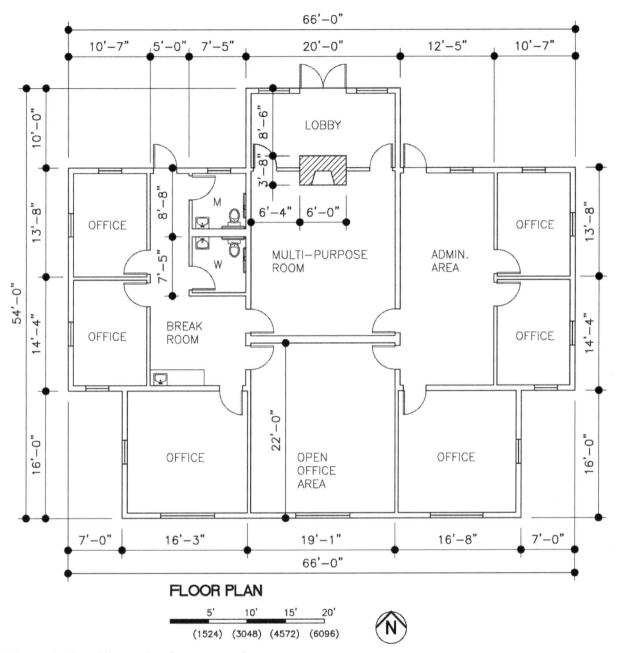

Figure 3.43   Floor plan for case study

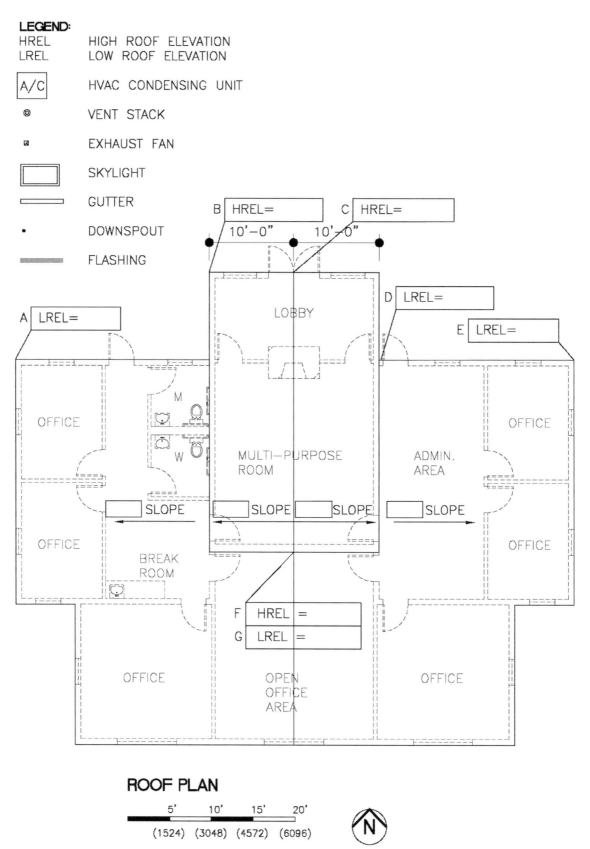

Figure 3.44   Roof plan with minimum slopes for case study

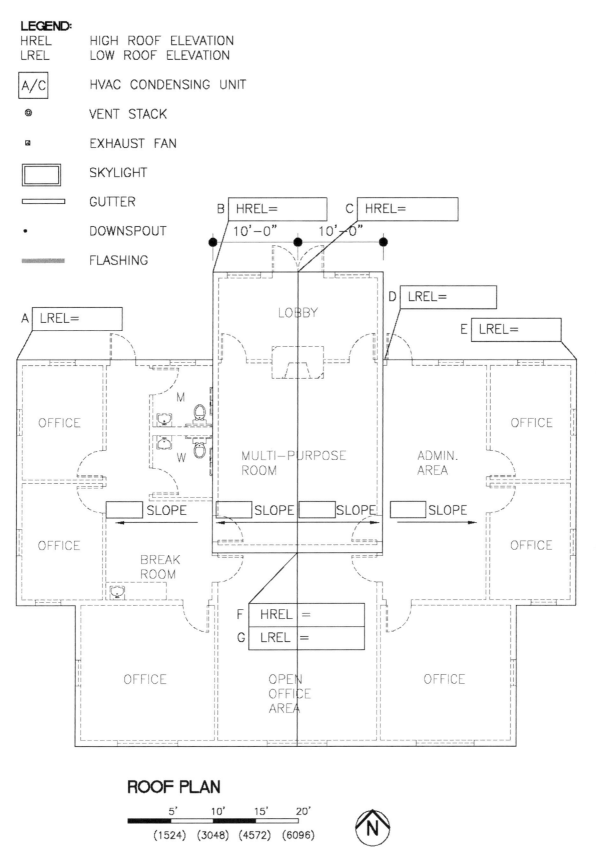

ROOF PLAN

Figure 3.45   Roof plan with *maximum* slopes and the *updated minimum* spot elevations

111. In figure 3.44, fill in the blanks to show the minimum slopes for the roofs allowed by the program.

112. In figure 3.44, fill in the blanks to show the minimum spot elevations (HREL & LREL) for the roofs allowed by the program.

113. In figure 3.44, drag and place the skylight(s) to meet the program requirements. You can use the skylight symbol more than once.

114. In figure 3.44, drag and place the HVAC condensing unit to meet the program requirements.

115. In figure 3.44, drag and place the vent stack to meet the program requirements. You can use the vent stack symbol more than once.

116. In figure 3.44, drag and place the exhaust fan to meet the program requirements. You can use the exhaust fan symbol more than once.

117. In figure 3.44, drag and place the flashing to meet the program requirements. You can use the flashing symbol more than once.

118. In figure 3.44, drag and place the gutter to meet the program requirements. You can use the gutter symbol more than once.

119. In figure 3.44, drag and place the downspout to meet the program requirements. You can use the downspout symbol more than once.

120. In figure 3.45, fill in the blanks to show the maximum slopes for the roofs allowed by the program. Use the maximum slopes to calculate and fill in the blanks to show the minimum spot elevations (HREL & LREL) for the roofs allowed by the program.

Chapter Four

ARE Mock Exam Solutions for
Project Development & Documentation (PDD) Division

A. Mock Exam Answers and Explanations: Multiple-Choice (MC)

Note: If you answer 60% of the questions correctly, you will pass the exam.

1. Answer: a and d
   Stainless steel nails and terne-coated stainless steel can be specified to affix shingles onto a roof structure. **Terne** is an alloy coating that used to be made from 20% tin and 80% lead. Currently, lead is not desirable in the construction industry. It has been replaced with the metal zinc and terne is made of 50% tin and 50% zinc. Terne metal must be painted. Well-maintained painted terne metal can last 90 years or more.

   Iron nails are not resistant to corrosion, and are NOT a good choice.

   Pneumatic staple guns can result in crushing the wood fibers, in shooting staples through the shingles, or in cracking the shingle. They are not a good choice either.

2. Answer: b and d
   Lead-based paint and asbestos have been banned in new construction since the late 1970s because they are hazardous materials.

   Copper nails can be used. Zinc-based paint is just a **distractor**.

3. Answer: c
   Red-cedar shingles should not have direct contact with copper nails because a chemical reaction between the copper and the wood will reduce the life of the roof. Hot-dipped, aluminum, zinc-coated, or stainless steel nails should be used.

   4-ply roofing is built-up roofing. TPO roofing is one kind of single-ply roofing. They both can be used with copper nails.

   Fiberglass roofing can also be used with copper nails.

4. Answer: b and d
   Please note that we are looking for the **incorrect** answers.
   The following statements are incorrect, and therefore the correct answers:

- Control joints also serve as isolation or construction joints. (Control joints do NOT separate the slab completely, and their depths are normally ¼ of the slab thickness. Control joints can NOT serve as construction joints)
- Control joints normally run from the top of slab to the bottom of the slab. (Control joints normally do **NOT** run from the top of slab to the bottom of the slab. their depths are normally ¼ of the slab thickness)

The following statements are correct, and therefore the incorrect answers:
- Construction joints also serve as isolation or control joints.
- Construction joints normally run from the top of slab to the bottom of the slab.

Control joints can be formed by saw cutting the concrete or by placing a 1/8" premolded strip insert when concrete is cast. They allow the concrete to crack along the predetermined lines.

5. Answer: a
   The term "fine sand float finish" refers to plastering.

   See the following link:
   http://www.omega-products.com/textures-2

   You need to read the information at the link above, and become familiar with various kinds of plaster finishes. This will not only help you pass ARE, but also help you in real architectural practice. Plaster finishes are normally noted on building exterior elevations.

   Paving, painting, and concrete are all **distractors**.

6. Answer: b
   The term "VOC" refers to Volatile Organic Compound. The word "Volatile" describes a liquid that evaporates at room temperature, and the word "organic" means a compound that contains carbon.

   Valid Organic Compound, Volatile Original Compound, and Volatile Original Composite are all **distractors**.

7. Answer: d
   Plastering is the most cost-effective finish for exterior walls.

8. Answer: a
   According to *International Building Code* (IBC), the handrails shall extend at least 12" (305) beyond the top riser and continue to slope for the depth of one tread beyond the bottom riser.

   See Section 1014.6 of *International Building Code* (IBC).
   See following link for the FREE IBC code sections citations:
   http://codes.iccsafe.org

9. Answer:
   According to *International Building Code* (IBC), stair riser heights shall be 7" (178) maximum and 4" (102) minimum. Rectangular stair tread depths shall be 11" (279) minimum.

   See Section 1011.5.2, Riser height and thread depth, of *International Building Code* (IBC).

   See following link for the FREE IBC code sections citations:
   http://codes.iccsafe.org

10. Answer: c
    The term "Elastomeric - Modified Acrylic" is most likely to be found in the specifications for **painting**. Elastomeric means elastic. Acrylic means a paint containing acrylic resin

11. Answer: c
    She should add a cricket on the **high** side of the roof next to the chimney to drain and divert the rainwater away from the chimney.

    Rainwater flows from high to low, so there is no point of adding a cricket on the **low** side of the roof next to the chimney.

    A cricket should ALWAYS be placed on the **high** side of the roof next to the chimney, HVAC units, and condensing units to divert the rainwater.

12. Answer: b and c
    The following is true about travel distance:
    • A travel distance is measured from the most remote point within a story.
    • When the path of exit access includes unenclosed stairway, the distance of travel on the stair shall be included in the travel distance measurement.

    The following is not true about travel distance:
    • A travel distance is measured from the door of the most remote room within a story.
    • When the path of exit access includes unenclosed stairway, the distance of travel on the stair shall not be included in the travel distance measurement.

    See *International Building Code* (IBC).

    See following link for the FREE IBC code sections citations:
    http://codes.iccsafe.org

13. Answer: a and c
    An architect is preparing the plan check package for a retail store. If the store sells any kinds of food including fresh produce, meat and candies (pre-package food), the architect probably needs to submit the plans to Health Department for plan check.
    The following statements are true:

- If the store sells fresh produce and meat, the architect probably needs to submit the plans to Health Department for plan check.
- If the store sells candies, the architect probably needs to submit the plans to Health Department for plan check.

The following statements are not true:

- If the store sells clothing, the architect probably needs to submit the plans to Health Department for plan check. (clothing is not food, Health Department is typically not interested in checking plans for stores that do not sell foods)
- If the store sells candies, the architect probably does not need to submit the plans to Health Department for plan check.

14. Answer: b
The Herringbone pattern/letter on the previous image is likely to have the highest construction cost because it is the most complicated pattern and takes the most labor to build.

15. Answer: c
The purpose of the weep holes at the bottom of the CMU retaining walls is to drain water from the bottom of the retaining wall. All other answers are distracters.

16. Answer: b and c
The following statements are true:
- Single-glass windows typically have a lower R-value than double-glass windows.
- Single-glass windows typically have a higher U-value than double-glass windows

R-value indicates a material's ability to resist heat flow. Higher R-value indicates the better ability to resist heat flow.

U-value indicates a material's ability to transfer heat. Higher U-value indicates the better ability to transfer heat.

17. Answer: c
For hydraulic elevators, the depth of the piston cylinder well is equal to the height of elevator travel.

A hydraulic elevator does NOT need a penthouse, but it has lower speed and is limited to six-story height because of the piston length.

18. Answer: a and c
For a site with underground methane gas, the following statements are true:
- The contractor should use special construction techniques to avoid explosion at the site. (Methane is the major component of natural gas. Methane gas is highly combustible. Any normal construction techniques that can generate sparks or fire are prohibited for the danger of job site fire or explosion.)

- The contractor can use underground-perforated pipes to collect the methane gas. (The perforated pipes can collect the methane gas, and then vent the methane gas at a certain height above roof.)

The following statements are not true:
- The contractor should have his employee use special masks at the site. (The contractor does NOT need to have his employee use special masks at the site.)
- The contractor can use automatic vent damper devices to alleviate the methane gas problem. (Automatic vent damper devices are used to regulate airflow of the HVAC system. They have nothing to do with methane gas and can NOT alleviate the methane gas problem.)

19. Answer: c
Warm air and/or moisture would create condensation on the vapor barrier.

The vapor barrier should be installed on the **warm** side of the walls to prevent condensation from being absorbed into the insulation. In most cases, the warm side of the walls occurs on the **inside** of the wall insulation, but for an air-conditioned building in hot and humid climate, the warm side of the wall occurs on the **outside** of the wall insulation.

20. Answer: d
Architects often specify Type "X" Gypsum Wallboard for fire resistance. Type "X" Gypsum Board is more expensive than regular gypsum wallboard, and is NOT easier to install than regular gypsum wallboard. It has no recyclability.

21. Answer: a
The image A shows a Fink truss.

The image B shows a king post truss.
The image C shows a queen post truss.
The image D shows a scissor truss.
The image E shows a Warren truss.
The image F shows a Howe truss.
The image G shows a Pratt truss.

22. Answer: d
The image D shows a right-hand door.
The image A shows a left-hand reverse door.
The image B shows a right-hand reverse door.
The image C shows a left-hand door.

23. Answer: b and c
If some of the exposed beams of an historic building have deflection, the following are recommended:

- Augmenting or upgrading
- Protecting and maintaining the beams and ensuring that structural members are free from insect infestation.

The following are not recommended:
- Leaving them in place without doing anything (This creates a life safety issue.)
- Replacement of <u>all</u> the beams (Repairing or limited replacement of <u>deflected</u> beams is appropriate.)

See pages 42 and 43 of the PDF file for *The Secretary of the Interior's Standards for the Treatment of Historic Properties with Guidelines for Preserving, Rehabilitating Restoring & Reconstructing Historic Buildings* at the following links:
http://www.ironwarrior.org/ARE/Historic_Preservation/

24. Answer: c and d
The following are not recommended when working on preservation of the interior of a historic building:
- Using propane to remove paint (Using destructive methods such as propane or butane torches or sandblasting to remove paint or other coatings is not recommended.)
- Sandblasting of character-defining features

The following are recommended when working on the interior of a historic building:
- Installing protective coverings for wall coverings in the corridors
- Replacement of broken window glazing (Changing the texture and patina of character-defining features through sandblasting or use of abrasive methods to remove paint, discoloration or plaster is not recommended.)

See pages 45 and 46 of the PDF file for *The Secretary of the Interior's Standards for the Treatment of Historic Properties with Guidelines for Preserving, Rehabilitating Restoring & Reconstructing Historic Buildings* at the following links:
http://www.ironwarrior.org/ARE/Historic_Preservation/

25. Answer: c
Image C shows the correct location of perforated pipe. The main purpose of the perforated pipe is to collect the water from the retaining portion of soil behind the retaining wall, and slopes and drains the water to an outlet away from wall.

26. Answer: b
The image shows a rigid frame: the connections between the beam and the columns are rigid.

The following are incorrect answers:

- Column and beam (The connections between the beam and the columns are flexible, and the column-and-beam assembly is NOT able to resist lateral forces.)
- Space frame (a planar unit consists of rigid, short linear members assembled into a three-dimensional triangle pattern)
- Prefabricated column and beam (The connections between the beam and the columns are flexible, and the column-and-beam assembly is NOT able to resist lateral forces.)

27. Answer: c
The image C shows a Sash door.

The image A shows a French door.
The image B shows a Glass door.
The image D shows a Panel door.

28. Answer: c
Firestopping is the correct term for A in the previous image. The **fireproofing** around the wide flange steel beam is a major clue for the correct answer.

Firestopping is required to seal off the gap between the wall and the edge of each floor. It has to be secured to the structure. Firestopping can consist of metal lath and plaster, steel plate and grout, or mineral wool safing.

29. Answer: a
In a fast-track, one-story project, roof framing system design is most likely a critical path item because it involves coordination with HVAC system and takes the longest time and will affect the progress of other elements.

The following will all take less time:
- HVAC system design
- Interior finish selection
- Door selection

30. Answer: a and b
Grade beams are underground beams connecting isolated footings

The following situation shall utilize grade beams:
- At site with expansive soils (Grade beams can transfer the building load more evenly and prevent uneven settlement)
- At storefront with no solid walls (This situation typical requires a moment frame system, including grade beams because storefront with no solid walls does NOT have adequate shear walls to resist the lateral force.)

The following situation shall NOT utilize grade beams:
- At site with underground rock

The following situation may NOT utilize grade beams:

- At site in an inland area

31. Answer: b
Quirk miter is the correct term for the joint shown in image A.

The following are some basic veneer stone corner joints:
- Corner "L" (Image B)
- Slip corner (Image C)
- Butt joint (Image D)

32. Answer: a
Cripple studs is the correct term for A in the image.

The following are incorrect answers:
- King posts (A term for trusses, and NOT for studs at all)
- Transom studs (Invented distractor)
- Top studs (Invented distractor)

33. Answer: c
Square edge tongue and groove is the correct term for the wood siding A in the image.

The following are incorrect answers:
- Bevel (Wood siding B)
- Shiplap (Wood siding C)
- Channel rustic (Wood siding D)

34. Answer: Locate the centroid of the hatched area as shown in figure 3.11 and calculate to find that $x = \underline{9.70"}$.

The centroid is the "center of gravity" of a very thin and flat object or a plane surface. We select X-X axis as the convenient base of the object. The sum of the statical moment of all parts equals the statical moment of the whole object, and we treat the area of the hole in the object as a negative number (figure 4.1):

$$(6" \times 10")(13") + (10" \times 4")(5") + (-\pi \times 1^2)(13") = x(6" \times 10" + 10" \times 4" - \pi \times 1^2)$$

$$780 + 200 - 40.82 = x(60 + 40 - 3.14)$$

$$939.18 = x(96.86)$$

$$x = 939.18 / 96.86 = 9.70"$$

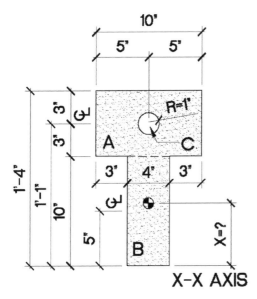

Figure 4.1   Locate the centroid of the hatched area

35. Answer: c
The reactions of the beam shown in figure 3.12 are
$R_1 = 1,300$ lbf, $R_2 = 4,700$ lbf.

Detailed calculations
Take the sum of the moment about R_1 to eliminate one of the unknown reactions and simplify the calculation.

Since the beam is statically determinate, the moment sum of the loads and reactions must equal zero.

(2,000 lbf) (4 ft) + (3,000 lbf) (8 ft) + [(500 plf) (2 ft)] (15 ft) – (10 ft) R_2 = 0

$R_2 = 4,700$ lbf

The sum of the loads must equal the reactions.
2,000 lbf + 3,000 lbf + (500 plf) (2 ft) = $R_1 + R_2$

6,000 lbf = $R_1 + 4,700$ lbf

$R_1 = 6,000$ lbf - 4,700 lbf = 1,300 lbf

36. Answer: b
Figure 3.13 shows a shear diagram of concentrated loads.
Upward forces are positive, and downward forces are negative. When there are no intervening loads between two concentrated loads, the portion of the shear diagram is a horizontal line. An intervening load causes a shear diagram to change abruptly vertically.

A shear diagram of uniformly distributed loads is a sloped line.

37. Answer: b
Figure 3.14 shows a **shear plate connector**. It has a flat plate with a flange extending from the face of the plate.

The following are incorrect answers:
- **split ring connector** (It has a cut-through ring to form a tongue and slot, but no flat plate.)
- double shear connector
- multiple shear connector

Figure 3.14 shows a single shear connector, not a double shear connector or a multiple shear connector.

38. Answer: a
Figure 3.15 shows a field weld; it is also welded all around.

The following are incorrect answers:
- flare weld
- bevel weld
- square weld

As an architect, you need to be able to read and understand the weld symbols. See the following links for more information:
http://en.wikipedia.org/wiki/File:Elements_of_a_welding_symbol.PNG
http://www.typesofwelding.net/weld_symbol.html
http://www.typesofwelding.net/weld_joints_symbol.html

You can also find information on weld joints and weld symbols in the *AISC Manual of Steel Construction*.

39. Answer: c
The structural steel shown in figure 3.16 is a "S" shape.

Look through the *AISC Manual of Steel Construction* and become familiar with the common steel shapes.

40. Answer: b and c
Because this is a simply supported beam, the section A-A shown in figure 3.17 has
- compression stresses in the top half of the beam, and
- tension stresses in the bottom half of the beam.

41. Answer: a and d
Because this is a cantilever beam, section A-A shown in figure 3.18 has
- tension stresses in the top half of the beam, and
- compression stresses in the bottom half of the beam.

Figure 3.18 is a very basic but important diagram, you really need to know it like the back of your hand.
section to use.

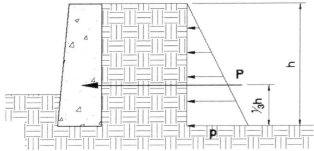

Figure 4.2   The pressure at the bottom of a retaining wall

42. Answer: b. 360 psf
See figure 4.2. The pressure at the bottom of the wall is P = (4 ft) (45 psf/ft) = 180 psf.

$$\textbf{The total horizontal load P} = \frac{\textbf{ph}}{\textbf{2}} = \frac{(180 \text{ psf}) (4 \text{ ft})}{2} = 360 \text{ psf}$$

The total load can be shown as acting on the centroid of a triangle, 1/3 the distance from the base.

43. Answer: b
For the same simple truss in figure 3.19, using the method of sections, the force in member BC is 7,500 lbf.

Our step-by-step solution is as follows. (figure 4.3)
1) Find the **reactions.**
Since all forces are symmetric, $R_A = R_F = \frac{1}{2}$ (3,000 lbf + 6,000 lbf + 3,000 lbf) = 6,000 lbf

2) Find the angle between member AB and AD.

$$\tan \theta = \frac{12 \text{ ft}}{16 \text{ ft}}$$

$$\theta = 36.87°$$

3) Find the moment arm of BC.
Since $\theta = 36.87°$ and the complementary angle is 53.13°. The difference of the angles = 53.13° - 36.87° = 16.26°.

$$\cos 16.26° = \frac{H}{10 \text{ ft}}$$

h = (10 ft) (cos 16.26°) = 9.60 ft

4) Take moments about point D to eliminate the two unknowns (F_{BD} and F_{AD}).
Note:
Because F_{BD} and F_{AD} pass through joint D, their moment arms equal zero, and therefore their moments equal zero as well. This is an important technique when using the method of sections.

By convention, moments acting clockwise are positive, and moments acting counterclockwise are negative. The sum of the moments about point D equal zero:
(6,000 lbf) (16 ft) - (3,000 lbf) (8 ft) – F_{Bc} (9.60 ft) = 0

F_{BC} = 7,500 lbf

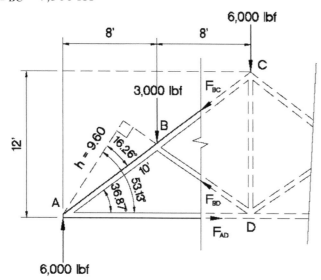

Figure 4.3   Method of sections

44. Answer: b
Figure 3.20 shows an anchor bolt. An anchor bolt has a "J" shape. As an architect, you need to be able to identify some very basic structural items.

The following are incorrect answers:
• lag screw
• hold-down bolt
• base plate screw

45. Answer: c
Figure 3.21 shows a hold-down bolt. A hold-down bolt has a "S" shape at the bottom.

The following are incorrect answers:
• lag screw
• anchor bolt
• base plate screw

46. Answer: c
    Plasticizers are used to reduce the amount of water needed for mixing concrete.

    The following are incorrect answers:
    - **Air-entraining agents** are used to form small dispersed bubbles in the concrete.
    - **Accelerators** are used to speed up hydration of concrete to achieve strength faster.
    - **Fine aggregates** are sand and small crushed rocks. They are part of the normal components of any concrete.

47. Answer: c
    Figure 3.22 shows a hold-down, a very common structural component. An architect should be able to identify it.
    The following are incorrect answers:
    - column base (typically a thin metal plate bent in a U-shape)
    - strap (typically a long and thin metal plate with holes for nailing)
    - structural plate

48. Answer: a and d
    6x6-10/10 and 6x6-W1.4x1.4 are two different designations for the same welded wire fabric (**WWF**) in English System. Welded wire fabric (**WWF**) is also called welded wire mesh (**WWM**).

    Welded wire fabric is a common reinforcement for concrete sidewalks. Becoming familiar with this material will help you in real architectural practice also.

    6x6-10/10 is the designation from an old system. 6x6 means the grid of the welded wire fabric is 6 inches x 6 inches, and 10/10 means the wire sizes are both 10 gauges. This old system is still in use.

    6x6-W1.4x1.4 is the designation from a new system. 6x6 means the grid of the welded wire fabric is 6 inches x 6 inches, W means it's smooth, and 1.4 means the cross-sectional wire area is 0.014 square inches. If the letter is D instead of W, it means the welded wire fabric is deformed.

    6x6-10/10 or 6x6-W1.4x1.4 is designated as 152x152-MW9.1/MW9.1 in the Metric System. The number 152 means 152 mm, and the number 9.1 means 9.1 mm^2.

    Again, 6x6-10/10 in the old system is equivalent to 6x6-W1.4x1.4 in the new English System. Many people want to know the detailed explanation. For those who are interested in the detailed information, here it is. You just need to look through this, and do not need to memorize.

    The wire sizes are the same in both systems but the old system gives the diameter of the wires which is 10 gauges (or 0.1350") and the new system gives the cross sectional area of the wire, 0.014 square inches. 10-gauge wire is 0.1350" in diameter and has a cross sectional area of 0.0143 square inches, and we can round it to 0.014 square inches.

Note:

The radius of 10-gauge wire =diameter/2 = 0.1350"/2 = 0.0675"

The cross sectional area of 10-gauge wire is:
A = π r^2 = 3.14 x (0.0675)^2 = 0.0143 square inches, and we can round it to 0.014 square inches

The grid size is:
6 inches = 6 x 25.4 mm = 152.40 mm, and we can round it to 152 mm

So, the 6x6 grid size in the new English System is equivalent to the 152x152 in the old system.

49. Answer: a
Diagram A shows the correct placement of rebar for the concrete beams of a gas station canopy supported by concrete columns.

Betweens the columns, there is positive moment in the beam and the rebar is placed close to the bottom.

At the columns and at the cantilever portions of the beam, there is negative moment in the beam and the rebar is bent and placed close to the top.

50. Answer: b
Using Method II, diagram B shows the correct direction of wind pressure.

Method II is the normal force method. It assumes that wind pressure acts simultaneously on all exterior surfaces. The windward walls have positive pressures acting toward the surfaces. The roof and leeward walls have negative pressures acting away from the surfaces.

Most of the questions of the ARE PDD division test your understanding of basic concepts. This question is a good example to demonstrate this fact.

In real practice, you also need to know basic structural concepts like the direction of wind pressures, but you will NOT need to do detailed calculations. The detailed calculations are part of your structural engineers' job.

NCARB expects the same knowledge since you need to be able to function as an average architect after you pass the ARE exams.

51. Answer: a
Diagram A is a correct depiction of wind loads on a diaphragm.

The windward edge of the floor/roof has a compression chord force, and the leeward edge of the floor/roof has a tension chord force.

52. Answer: a
In reference to figure 3.26, the brace at location A is in tension, and the brace at location B is not stressed.

If the wind direction reverses, the brace at location B is in tension, and the brace at location A is not stressed.

K-braces are often placed at the center bay and act as vertical trusses cantilevered out of the ground.

53. Answer: c
Site Class A, B, C, D, E, or F in Chapter 16 of IBC is based on soil properties.

See related section of IBC Chapter 16 at the following link:
http://publiccodes.cyberregs.com/icod/ibc/2006f2/icod_ibc_2006f2_16_par120.htm

54. Answer: b
For a hospital, the Important Factor (I Factor) for **snow** is **1.2**, For earthquakes it is 1.5, and for wind it is 1.15.
You do not have to remember all these numbers for every building type, but you need to be familiar with them. Since hospitals belong to one of the most important occupancy groups, you need to know them well.

55. Answer: The section modulus for the geometric section shown in figure 3.27 is <u>94.78</u> in^3.

If you really understand the formulas given in the question, it is very easy to come up with the solution. Here is our step-by-step solution.

*Note: The formula I = bd^3/12 is for **rectangular** sections ONLY, and is for the moment of inertia about the centroidal axis **parallel to the base**.*

1) We can use the formula I = bd^3/12 to calculate the moment of inertia for the big 8"x12" rectangle first:
I_b = bd^3/12 = 8 x 12^3/12 = 1152 in^4

2) We can use the formula I = bd^3/12 to calculate the moment of inertia for the two small 3.5"x10" rectangles as shown with a hatched pattern in figure 4.6.
I_s = bd^3/12 = 3.5 x 10^3/12 = 291.67 in^4

3) To get the moment of inertia for the geometric section shown in figure 3.27, we can subtract the moment of inertia for the two small rectangles from the big rectangle.
   $I = I_b - 2I_s = 1152$ in^4 - (2 x 291.67 in^4) = 568.67 in^4

4) To get the section modulus (S) for the geometric section shown in figure 3.27
   $S = I/C = 568.67$ in^4/6 in = 94.78 in^3

Note: C is the distance from the neutral axis (centroidal axis) to the outmost part of the section (extreme fiber). It equals 6" as shown in figure 4.4.

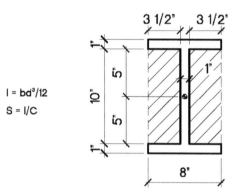

Figure 4.4   Section modulus

56. Answer: The live load for the floor supported by the column as shown in figure 3.28 is <u>75</u> kips (kg).

Each side of the column supports half a bay of the floor (figure 4.5). Therefore, the area supported by the column is: 30' x 50' = 1,500 sf.

The live load for the floor supported by the column as shown in figure 3.28 is:
1,500 sf x 50 psf = 75,000p = 75 kips

All the other formulas and data shown in figure 3.28 are simply **distracters** used to confuse. They are NOT needed for the solution. This is a technique actually used by NCARB for the real ARE exams.

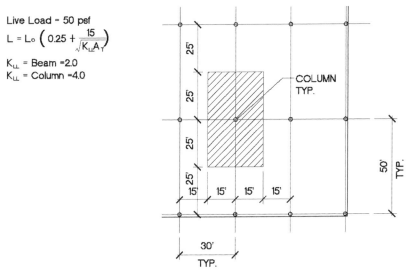

Live Load = 50 psf

$$L = L_o \left(0.25 + \frac{15}{\sqrt{K_{LL} A_T}} \right)$$

K_{LL} = Beam = 2.0
K_{LL} = Column = 4.0

Figure 4.5   The live load for the floor supported by the column

57. Answer: c
The tendency of a solid material to move slowly or deform permanently under the influence of sustained stress is called **creep** or **deformation**.

The following are incorrect answers and used as **distracters**:
- shrinkage
- temperature expansion
- contraction

58. Answer: b
When the ratio of a slab's length (long direction to short direction) is greater than <u>2:1</u> it can be considered a one-way slab.

A one-way slab typically only has moment-resisting reinforcement along its short-direction. The moment along its long-direction is very small and can be omitted.

59. Answer: b
B is an eccentrically braced frame (EBF).

Braced frames are designed to have its members work in tension and compression, similar to a truss. Braced frames often have steel members. Most braced frames are **concentric braced frames**, which means that where their members intersect at a node, the centroid of each member passes through the same point.

Concentric braced frames are either **ordinary concentric braced frames (OCBF)** or **special concentric braced frames (SCBF)**. OCBF are often used in areas of low seismic risk.

Special concentric braced frames (SCBF) are also called **eccentrically braced frames (EBF).** The work points of the diagonal members of an EBF are moved so that the diagonal members are connected to a beam a short distance from the "node" where the beam and column intersect (figure 3.29, Diagram B).

For EBF, there is moment in a beam due to lateral forces. EBF are used in areas of high seismic risk.

In figure 3.29, Diagram A shows an ordinary concentric braced frame (OCBF). Diagram C and D show regular **moment-resistant framing (MRF).**

60. Answer: d
For the flexible diaphragm shown in figure 3.30, the shear at F_2 = 30 kips.

A **flexible diaphragm** is one with a maximum lateral deformation more than two times the average story drift of the same story. For a flexible diaphragm, the lateral load and the related shear are distributed per the tributary area. See figure 4.6.

If we assume the length of the building is "L," then the tributary area for F_2 is (shown with hatched pattern in figure 4.6)
L(15' + 15') = 30L

The overall area of the building is
L(30' + 30') = 60L

The shear at F_2 = 60 kips (30L/60L) = 30 kips.

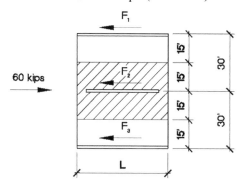

Figure 4.6   A flexible diaphragm

61. Answer: b
If resisted only by gravity forces, the factor of safety against overturning for a concrete shear wall as shown in figure 3.31 is 6.91.

1) **Calculate the overturning moment (OM)**
You must use the bottom of the footing to calculate and check the factor of safety (figure 4.7).
OM = Force x Distance = 30 kips x (30 ft + 3 ft) = 990 kip-ft

2) Calculate the stabilizing moment (SM)

The question does not mention if the 300k of dead load includes the weight of the concrete wall and footing.

We can try to calculate it both ways.

- **Assume the 300 kips of dead load (DL) includes the weight of the concrete wall and footing.**
  The distance to the pivot point A is 12.5'.
  SM = DL x Distance = 300 kips x 12.5' = 3,750 kip-ft
  Factor of safety = SM/OM = (3,750 kip-ft)/(990 kip-ft) = 3.79

- **Assume the 300 kips of dead load (DL) does NOT include the weight of the concrete wall and footing.**
  The weight of the concrete wall = (20' x 30' x 2') x 0.15 kips/ft^3 = 180 kips
  The weight of the concrete footing = (25' x 3' x 6') x 0.15 kips/ft^3 = 67.5 kips

  The distance to the pivot point A is 12.5'.
  SM = (DL + The weight of the concrete wall + The weight of the concrete footing) x Distance = (300 kips +180 kips + 67.5 kips) x 12.5' = 6,843.75 kip-ft
  Factor of safety = SM/OM = (6,843.75 kip-ft)/(990 kip-ft) = 6.91

3) 6.91 is the correct answer since it matches choice "b" and 3.79 is not an option.

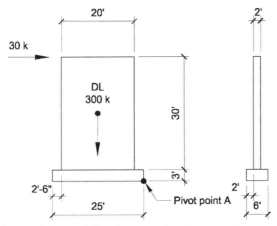

Figure 4.7   The factor of safety against overturning for a concrete shear wall

62. Answer: a and c
The following are methods used to determine wind loads on a structure (figure 4.8):
- **Normal force method (also called ASCE 7 Method II, the Analytical Procedure)** assumes wind pressures act simultaneously normal (perpendicular) to all exterior surfaces. For the leeward side, the height is taken at the mean roof height and the pressure is considered constant for the full height of the building. The normal force

method can be used for any structure, and is the ONLY method for gabled frames with rigid joints.

Note: ASCE means American Society of Civil Engineers

- **Projected area method (also called ASCE 7 Method I, Simplified Method)** assumes that horizontal pressures act on the complete vertical projected area of the building and that vertical pressure acts simultaneously on the complete horizontal projected area. The projected area method can be used for any structure less than 200 feet high EXCEPT for gabled frames with rigid joints.

The following are invented terms used as distracters:
- lateral force method
- diagram method

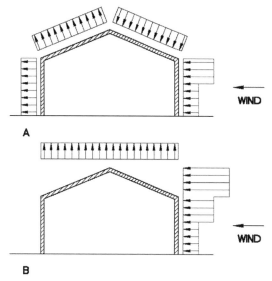

Figure 4.8   Methods to determine wind loads

63. Answer: b and c

The following statements regarding earthquakes are true:
- P wave is a primary wave that alternately pushes (compresses) and pulls (dilates) the rock.
- P waves, just like acoustic waves, are able to travel through solid rock, such as granite and alluvium; through soils; and through liquids, such as volcanic magma or the water of lakes and oceans.

The following are incorrect answers:
- P wave is a wave that moves perpendicular to the ground surface.
- S waves, just like acoustic waves, are able to travel through solid rock, such as granite and alluvium; through soils; and through liquids, such as volcanic magma or the water of lakes and oceans.

Per Chapter 2, Section 2.3.2, Types of Earthquake Waves of **FEMA publication number 454 (FEMA454),** *Designing for Earthquakes: A Manual for Architects*:

"The first two types of waves travel through the body of the earth before arriving at the surface. The faster of these "body" waves is appropriately called the **primary** or **P wave.** Its motion is the same as that of a sound wave in that, as it spreads out, it alternately pushes (compresses) and pulls (dilates) the rock. These P waves, just like acoustic waves, are able to travel through solid rock, such as granite and alluvium, through soils, and through liquids, such as volcanic magma or the water of lakes and oceans.

The second and slower seismic body wave through the earth is called the **secondary** or **S wave** or sometimes the **shear wave.** As an S wave propagates, it shears the rocks sideways at right angles to the direction of travel. At the ground surface, the upward emerging S waves also produce both vertical and horizontal motions. Because they depend on elastic shear resistance, S waves ca<u>nnot</u> propagate in liquid parts of the earth, such as lakes. As expected from this property, their size is significantly weakened in partially liquefied soil. The speed of both P and S seismic waves depends on the density and elastic properties of the rocks and soil through which they pass. In earthquakes, P waves move faster than S waves and are felt first. The effect is similar to a sonic boom that bumps and rattles windows. Some seconds later, S waves arrive with their significant component of side-to-side shearing motion...for upward wave incidence, the ground shaking in the S waves becomes both vertical and horizontal, which is the reason that the S wave motion is so effective in damaging structures."

64. Answer: The three basic alternative types of vertical lateral force–resisting systems are **shear walls, braced frames,** and **moment-resistant frames.**

There are two general types of **braced frames:** conventional concentric and eccentric. In the **concentric frame**, the centerlines of the bracing members meet the horizontal beam at a single point. In the **eccentric braced frame**, the braces are deliberately designed to meet the beam some distance apart from one another. The short piece of beam between the ends of the braces is called a link beam. The purpose of the link beam is to provide ductility to the system. Under heavy seismic forces, the link beam will distort and dissipate the energy of the earthquake in a controlled way, thus protecting the remainder of the structure.

See Chapter 5, 5.2.1, The Vertical Lateral Resistance Systems, of **FEMA publication number 454 (FEMA454),** *Designing for Earthquakes: A Manual for Architects.*

65. Answer: d
Inland waterways belong to wind exposure category D per ASCE 7.

ASCE 7 is a book entitled *Minimum Design Loads for Buildings and Other Structures*, published by ASCE (American Society of Civil Engineers). You can purchase it from Amazon, but I doubt you'll refer to it a lot in practice, because you normally leave the detailed structural calculations to your structural engineer.

Per ASCE 7, 1609.4 & 6.5.6 Exposure Categories are defined as follows.

- **Exposure A** is no longer used in ASCE 7.
- **Exposure B** is used as the default.
- **Exposure C** includes shorelines of hurricane prone regions (no longer Exposure D).
- **Exposure D** now only applies to inland waterways, Great Lakes, Coastal California, Oregon, Washington, and Alaska.

See page 20 of the PDF file of "Wind Design Made Simple" by ICC TRI-Chapter Uniform Code Committee available for FREE at the following link: http://www.calbo.org/Documents/SimplifiedWindHandout.pdf

IBC also has similar definitions.
"An exposure category shall be determined in accordance with the following:

Exposure B. Exposure B shall apply where the ground surface roughness condition, as defined by Surface Roughness B, prevails in the upwind direction for a distance of at least 2,600 feet (792 m) or 20 times the height of the building, whichever is greater.

Exception: For buildings whose mean roof height is less than or equal to 30 feet (9144 mm), the upwind distance is permitted to be reduced to 1,500 feet (457 m).

Exposure C. Exposure C shall apply for all cases where Exposures B or D do not apply.

Exposure D. Exposure D shall apply where the ground surface roughness, as defined by Surface Roughness D, prevails in the upwind direction for a distance of at least 5,000 feet (1524 m) or 20 times the height of the building, whichever is greater. Exposure D shall extend inland from the shoreline for a distance of 600 feet (183 m) or 20 times the height of the building, whichever is greater."

See related IBC information for FREE at the following link:
http://codes.iccsafe.org

66. Answer: c
Figure 3.32 shows a reinforced concrete wall. The following statement is correct:
- Pier 1 and Pier 4 resist more lateral load than Pier 2 and Pier 3.

The following are incorrect answers:
- Pier 1 and Pier 2 resist more lateral load than Pier 3 and Pier 4.
- Pier 1 and Pier 3 resist more lateral load than Pier 2 and Pier 4.
- Pier 3 and Pier 4 resist more lateral load than Pier 1 and Pier 2.
- Each pier resists the same lateral load.

The lateral load will be distributed to the piers according to their rigidities. Rigidity is defined as resistance to deflection. For a reinforced concrete wall, the rigidity is determined by the width to height ratio. Since all piers have the same height (4 feet), the wider pier will have a greater rigidity. Pier 1 and Pier 4 are both 8 feet wide, and Pier 2 and Pier 3 are both 6 feet wide, so, Pier 1 and Pier 4 resist more lateral load than Pier 2 and Pier 3.

67. Answer: c
Figure 3.33 shows a 2-story room addition to a 1-story existing building. The following statement is correct:
- Column C will resist more lateral load than the other columns.

The following are incorrect answers:
- Column A will resist more lateral load than the other columns.
- Column B will resist more lateral load than the other columns.
- Column D will resist more lateral load than the other columns.
- Each column resists the same lateral load.

This room addition project accidentally created a "short column" condition at column C. Because column C is shorter and more rigid than the other columns, it will resist more lateral load and has a greater risk of failure.

The weakest location is at the connection of columns B and C.

68. Answer: c
Figure 3.34 shows a 3-story moment-resisting frame with hinged bases resisting lateral loads. Ignoring the dead load, tension in one hinge base and compression in another hinge base resist the overturning caused by the lateral loads (figure 4.9).

The following are incorrect answers:
- shear in the columns (Shear in the columns does NOT resist the overturning.)
- moment at the column bases (There is no moment at any hinged bases.)
- tension in the beams (The beams have no tension since we ignore the dead loads.)
- compression in the beams (Compression in the beams does NOT resist the overturning.)

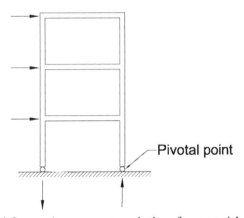

Figure 4.9   A moment-resisting frame with hinged bases resisting lateral loads

69. Answer: f and h
Referring to the same 3-story moment-resisting frame as shown in figure 3.34, if we include the dead load, the following resist the overturning caused by the lateral loads:

- weight of a column and beams (This answer was placed at the end to make sure you were patient enough to read all the choices. See figure 4.10.)
- tension or compression in one hinge base, and compression in another hinge base (Because we include the dead loads, one of the hinge bases has compression, but the other hinge base may have tension OR compression, depending on the actual amount of the dead load.)

The following are incorrect answers:
- shear in the columns
- weight of the columns (This answer is not complete. It does not include the weight of the beams.)
- moment at the column bases (There is no moment at hinge base.)
- tension in one hinge base, and compression in another hinge base
- tension in the beams
- compression in the beams

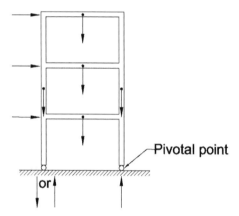

Figure 4.10   A moment-resisting frame with hinged bases and dead loads resisting lateral loads

70. Answer: d

The rigid frame shown has moment-resisting connections and fixed bases, so both the upper corners and the two fixed bases are restrained against rotation, as shown in the correct answer, Diagram D.

If the column bases were hinged, the bases would provide no restraint against rotation, and Diagram B would be the correct answer.

71. Answer: a

A horizontal force of 25 kips is applied to a frame with diagonal braces made of cables as shown in figure 3.36. The internal tension in each brace is as follows:
- brace 1 = 0, brace 2 = 35.36 kips.

The key to this question is that diagonal braces made of cables can *only* resist tension, but not compression. So, Brace 1 will always have zero stress since it cannot resist compression.

See the free body diagram as shown in figure 4.11.

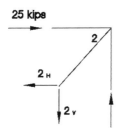

Fig 4.13

Figure 4.11   Free body diagram of a frame

$\sum H = 0$

+ 25kips - 2_H = 0

2_H = 25 kips

Since the frame is 16' wide and 16' high, the brace is at an 45° angel, so 2_v = 25 kips

Therefore, the tension in brace 1 = $\sqrt{25^2 + 25^2}$ = 35.36 kips

72. Answer: b and d
Systems B and D shown in figure 3.37 are stable under lateral forces.

System A will collapse under vertical or lateral forces or the dead load of the members. System C will collapse under lateral forces.

73. Answer: d
The net uplift at point 1 is zero.

We take moment at point 2:
Overturning moment = 500 lb x 10 ft = 5,000 ft-lb

Dead load resisting moment = 500 lb x 20 ft = 10,000 ft-lb > Overturning moment

Therefore, there is zero uplift at Point 1.

74. Answer: 1/4" x 90 = 22.5" =1'-10 ½" or 1.875 feet (571.50)

75. Answer: a

Convection, thermal **radiation,** and heat **conduction** are three basic forms of heat transfer.

The transfer of heat via the movement of **fluids** is called **convection**. **Convection** is the dominant form of heat transfer in liquids and gases.

Thermal **radiation** is energy emitted by matter as electromagnetic waves. It is a direct result of the random movements of atoms and molecules in matter. It propagates without the presence of matter through the vacuum of space.

Heat **conduction** is heat transfer via the interaction of hot atoms and molecules with neighboring atoms and molecules, transferring some of their energy (heat) to these neighboring particles or as electrons move from one atom to another. It is the main form of heat transfer within a solid or between solid objects.

Mass transfer is the energy or heat transfer by physically moving a hot or cold object from one place to another, like placing hot water in a bottle or the movement of an iceberg in changing ocean currents.

76. Answer: b, c, d, and e

The human body can lose heat through:
- **evaporation,** the transmission of heat via the process of moisture changing to vapor.
- **conduction,** the transmission of heat through direct contact.
- **convection,** the transmission of heat via the movement of a fluid (liquid or gas).
- **radiation,** the transmission of heat through electromagnetic waves from a warm surface to a cooler surface.

Ventilation and condensation are just distracters.

77. Answer: **Water hammer** is a pressure surge that can occur when water is shut off or forced to change direction abruptly. It can cause noise, vibration, or pipe collapse. **Capped air chambers** or **manufactured shock absorbers** are often used at fixture branches to alleviate this problem.

78. Answer: b and d

The following statements are true:
- Roof drains should be connected to a storm drain if possible.
- A grease interceptor can be connected to a sewer line.

Overflow drains should NEVER be connected to a storm drain. They should be spilled at about 8" above exterior grade and at locations that can be easily noticed by building users. Their purpose is to drain the rainwater from the roof if the roof drains become clogged. If rainwater starts to drain from the overflow drains, it means either the roof drains are clogged, or there is too much rain. Excessive ponding of rainwater could cause the roof to collapse; the building users should be able to notice this condition and have the problem fixed right away.

A floor drain can NEVER be connected to a sewer line. A floor drain collects graywater, while a sewer is for black water. These two distinct types of water should never be mixed together.

A grease interceptor can be connected to a sewer line because its purpose is to intercept the grease from kitchen sinks.

The following concepts are VERY important:

Potable water is clean water used for human consumption.

Graywater is household water that has not come into contact with kitchen sinks, human excretion, or animal waste. Graywater includes used water from bathroom washbasins, bathtubs, showers, and water from laundry tubs and clothes washers. Graywater does not include water from dishwashers or kitchen sinks.

Blackwater, otherwise known as brown water, foul water, or sewage, is water from the kitchen sink, dishwasher, or water that has come into contact with human or animal waste.

NEVER mix the plumbing system for potable water, graywater, or blackwater.

79. Answer: A pipe with a maximum of 5 ½ inches outside diameter can fit inside a 6" wood stud wall.

    A 6" <u>wood</u> stud wall is a <u>nominal</u> dimension, and the actual dimension of the wood stud is 5 ½". On the other hand, a 6" <u>metal</u> stud wall is a <u>real</u> dimension, and the actual dimension of the metal stud is 6".

80. Answer: c
    A 2" copper pipe means the inner diameter of the pipe is a little larger than 2" due to historical reasons.

    In the 1930s, the copper pipe was designated by its inner diameter and a 1/16" (1.6) wall thickness. For example, a 2-inch (50.80) copper pipe had a 2 1/8" (54.61) outside diameter. With the development of technology, pipe walls became thinner, but the outside diameter stayed the same so it could mate with existing older pipes, increasing the inner diameter beyond two inches.

    The sizes and history of cast iron pipes and plastic pipes are similar.

81. Answer: b
For a faucet in a house, a globe valve is most likely used.

The following are some common valve types and their uses:

- A **gate valve** is used where control is either completely off or on, and has a low friction loss.
- A **globe valve** is used where water is frequently controlled and water flow varies such as at hose bibs or faucets, and has a high friction loss.
- A **check valve** allows water to flow in only one direction, preventing back flow and related water contamination.
- An **angle valve** is a globe valve with a built-in 90-degree turn.
- A **butterfly valve** is used for on-off operation of gas, water, air, and vacuum line. This valve features a quarter-turn. In homes, it is often used as the shut-off valve near the water or gas meter.

See Architectural Graphic Standard for images of the different types of valves and learn to be able to identify them by their image.

82. Answer: a
A 120/240 V, single-phase, three-wire system is common for residences or smaller buildings; 240 V is for dryers and electric ranges.

A120/208 V, three-phase, four-wire system is frequently used for larger buildings and provides a variety of electrical loads.

A 277/480 V, three-phase, four-wire system is for even larger buildings, especially buildings with 277 V <u>fluorescent</u> lights, such as offices or shops. This system requires smaller, step-down transformers to provide 120 V services for outlets.

A 2400/4160 V, three-phase, four-wire system is for factories with machinery or very large commercial buildings.

83. Answer: b and d
Urinals and toilets contain human waste and are permitted to connect to a **<u>soil</u> stack vent.**

Lavatories and bidets do <u>NOT</u> contain human waste and are permitted to connect to a **waste stack vent**.

84. Answer: c
A handicapped accessible receptacle outlet is a minimum of 15" above the floor

Per *ADAAG Manual: A Guide to the American with Disabilities Accessibility Guidelines*, section 4.27.3, electrical and communications system receptacles on walls shall be mounted no less than 15 in (380 mm) above the floor.

85. Answer: d
Glass has the lowest coefficient of thermal expansion.

The coefficients of thermal expansion for some common piping material are as follows:
- PVC: 52
- Copper: 17
- Iron: 11.8
- Glass: 8.5

See the following link for further information:
http://en.wikipedia.org/wiki/Thermal_expansion

86. Answer: b and c
We are looking for <u>incorrect</u> statements.
The following statements regarding fixture installation and the transfer of luminaire's heat are <u>false</u> and therefore the correct answers:
- Surfaced-mounted fixtures transfer all their heat to the space, and they remain cool.
- Surfaced-mounted fixtures transfer about 50% their heat to the space, and they run hot.

(They transfer <u>all</u> their heat to the space, but run <u>hot</u> because this transfer is blocked upward.)

The following statements regarding fixture installation and the transfer of luminaire's heat are <u>true</u> and therefore the <u>in</u>correct answers:
- Suspended fixtures transfer all their heat to the space, and they remain cool.
- Completely recessed and enclosed fixtures transfer about 50% of their heat to the plenum.
- Baffled or open louvered fixtures transfer about 75% of their heat to the plenum.

87. Answer: c
The U-value for the wall is 0.0765 or approximately 0.08.

1) First seek the total resistance of the wall assembly (R_t) by adding together the R-values for each wall component.

Component	R-value
Outside air layer	0.17
3/4" Cement plaster, sand aggregate	0.15
½" Plywood	0.62
Nominal 3" batt fiberglass	11.00
Gypsum board	0.45
Inside air layer	0.68
R_t	**13.07**

2) The U-value of the wall assembly is then calculated with the following equation:
   $U = 1/ R_t = 1/13.07 = 0.0765$

88. Answer: c

The total room absorption should be approximately 75 sabins to achieve optimum reverberation time.

$T_R = 0.35$ s

$V = 22'\text{-}0'' \times 20'\text{-}0'' \times 12'\text{-}0'' = 5280$ ft^3

For English system: K = 0.05 (See the BS division PDF reference sheet downloaded from NCARB website listed on page 23.)

Based on NCARB reference sheet:
$T_R = K \times V/\sum A$

$\sum A = K \times V/T_R = 0.05 \times 5280/0.35 = 754.3$ or approximately 750 sabins.

89. Answer: b

A normal human being can hear sound in the range of 20 Hz to 20,000 Hz.

90. Answer: c

The R-value for the opaque wall is approximately 30.

$U_w = 0.35$
$U_o = 0.086$

$A_w = (3'\text{-}0'' \times 5'\text{-}0'') \times 5$ windows = 75 s.f.
$A_o = 9'\text{-}0'' \times 50'\text{-}0'' = 450$ s.f.
$A_{op} = A_o - A_w = 450$ s.f. - 75 s.f. = 375 s.f.

Per the reference sheet provided by NCARB:
$U_o = [(U_w \times A_w) + (U_{op} \times A_{op})]/A_o$

$U_o \times A_o = (U_w \times A_w) + (U_{op} \times A_{op})$

$U_{op} \times A_{op} = (U_o \times A_o) - (U_w \times A_w)$

$U_{op} = [(U_o \times A_o) - (U_w \times A_w)]/A_{op} = [(0.086 \times 450) - (0.35 \times 75)]/375$
$= (38.7 - 26.25)/375 = 12.45/375 = 0.0332$

$R_{op} = 1/U_{op} = 1/0.0332 = 30.10$ or approximately 30

91. Answer: A

Building A shown in figure 3.40 will most likely benefit the most from seeking LEED certification because it currently consumes the greatest amount of electricity of the four. Seeking LEED certification will likely reduce the energy use or electricity use for this building.

92. Answer: c. 112.00'

Because the front door has a threshold, the proper spot elevation at the front entrance has to be 112.00'. Otherwise, the front entrance will exceed the maximum 1/4 inch to 1/2 inch vertical change in level and will not comply with the handicap codes.

See cross section drawings below:

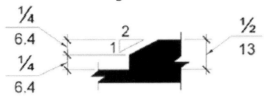

Figure 4.12   Bevel change in level

Source:

Figure303.3, Bevel Change in Level
http://www.access-board.gov/guidelines-and-standards/buildings-and-sites/about-the-ada-standards/ada-standards/chapter-3-building-blocks

Also see:
http://www.ada.gov/

AND
http://www.access-board.gov/guidelines-and-standards/buildings-and-sites/about-the-ada-standards/ada-standards

93. Answer: b. 111.98'

For the same one-story supermarket building in previous question, 111.96' is a proper spot elevation at the front entrance if the front door has no threshold. This is because 1/4 inch (or 0.02') is the maximum vertical change in level: 112.00'-0.02' = 111.98'.

We set the spot elevation to as low as possible per the handicap codes to prevent water from getting into the building. The site walk near the front entrance also needs to slope away from the building at 1% to 2%. We suggest setting the slope at 1.5%.

94. Answer: c. Perforated pipe

B as shown on Figure 3.41 is perforated pipe. See explanation in answer to previous question.

95. Answer: c, d, and e

The following are acceptable ways to revise drawings and specifications during construction:
- Change orders
- Written orders for a minor change of the Work
- Construction Change directives

Addenda are ways to revise contract documents, including drawings and specifications before the bid is due. A punch list is a correction items prepared by the contractor for items he has not finished or to be corrected per the contract documents, including drawings and specifications, NOT a way to revise drawings and specifications during construction.

A **notice** is NOT an official AIA document.

96. Answer: d
All the following can affect a project's construction cost:
- Project location
- Schedule
- Type of construction
- LEED certification

97. Answer: d
An architect shall obtain the owner's approval before proceeding to the next phase of design.

The following three answers are distracters, and they are not correct:
- An architect shall assist the owner and issue modifications to contractors during bidding process. (An architect shall assist the owner and issue **Addenda**, NOT **modifications,** to contractors during bidding process, and **before** the execution of the construction contract. **Modifications** only occur **after** the execution of the construction contract, in the form of change orders, construction change directives, or an order for minor change in work. Make sure you know the difference between the Addenda and Modifications.)
- An architect just needs to prepare one estimate of the construction cost for the owner. (An architect needs to prepare estimates or updates of the estimates of the construction cost for the owner at the preliminary design, schematic design, design development, and construction documents phase as part of the **basic** architectural services)
- If an architect just needs to prepare an estimate of the construction cost for the owner, she should treat this as an additional service (See explanation for the previous item).

See the FREE PDF file of the commentary for B101–2007 (Former B141–1997), Standard Form of Agreement between Owner and Architect (RAIC Document 6) at the following link:
http://www.aia.org/contractdocs/aiab081438

98. Answer: c
These number keynotes refer to specification sections. If you are familiar with CSI MasterFormat specification sections, you should be able to answer this question correctly.

My other book, *Building Construction*, has detailed discussions on CSI MasterFormat specification sections.

Product codes, building code sections, and finish schedule codes are distracters.

99. Answer: b, d, and e

The architect does NOT need review **every** submittal submitted by the contractor. She just needs to review the submittals required by the construction documents. Other submittals not required by the construction documents submitted by the contractor can be returned without ANY action by the architect.

The architect issues Addenda before the bid is due, NOT during construction phase.

The contractor, NOT the architect, prepares the Punch List.

The architect conducts field observations and issues changes requested by the owner via Construction Change Directives or Change Orders during construction phase.

100. Answer: c, e, and f

Per A201–2007, General Conditions of the Contract for Construction, the following are contract documents:

- Supplementary Condition
- Drawings and Specifications
- Construction Change Directive

The following are NOT contract documents unless specifically enumerated in the agreement:

- Invitation to bid
- Instruction to Bidders
- Contractor's proposal

You can find a FREE PDF file of commentary for AIA document A201–2007, General Conditions of the Contract for Construction, at the following link: http://www.aia.org/contractdocs/aiab081438

101. Answer: c, d, e, and f

Architect's instrument of service includes every embodiment of the professional services that architect and his consultants provide, including project research and studies, sketches, drawings, and specifications. Structural, electrical, mechanical, and plumbing engineers are typically the architect's consultants, and their plans and specifications are part of the architect's instrument of service. Electrical single line diagram is part of the electrical plans and therefore part of architect's instrument of service.

Civil and geotechnical engineers are often owner's consultants, and civil plans and geotechnical studies are unlikely to be part of architect's instrument of service unless noted on the plans.

102. Answer: b

The contractor should pay the owner for monetary damages. The contractor can back charge his electrical subcontractor and the supplier of the electrical switchgear to recover the cost, but that is a separate issue.

The contractor has to pay the owner for monetary damages per the contract even if he may not be able to recover his cost.

According to **privity**, the electrical subcontractor and the supplier of the electrical switchgear are not a party to the contract to the owner, and they should not pay the owner directly.

103. Answer: b

The contractor should be responsible for this construction accident. If he has notified the owner and the architect to about his concerns <u>in writing instead of verbally</u>, and the owner instructs the contractor to proceed as the original construction documents, the owner would be responsible for the accident. See A201–2007, General Conditions of the Contract for Construction, Section 3.3.1.

104. Answer: b

Submittals are NOT a part of the contract documents. The architect's act of approving submittals does NOT relieve the contractor from its obligation of complying with the contract documents.

See FREE PDF file of commentary for AIA document A201–2007, General Conditions of the Contract for Construction.

105. Answer: d

Jobsite safety procedures are the contractor's sole responsibilities, but the architect should still notify the superintendent about her concerns. She should never instruct a subcontractor what to do. Notifying the owner may be helpful, but it is not the best answer.

106. Answer: b

The contractor should absorb the cost of the work. The contractor should submit bid based on the entire set of contract documents, NOT just portions. It is the contractor's responsibility to coordinate all subcontractors and submit a bid for the entire Work.

107. Answer: a

The contractor is not entitled to a change order. The project has started, and the contract must have been signed. The contractor must fulfill his responsibilities under the contract.

108. Answer: c

Yes, the contractor had finished the project within the contract time because the substantial completion occurred within 180 days of the commencement of the work (January 15, 2009).

The date of the commencement of the work is the date established in the agreement, NOT the actual date the contractor start the work.

Contract time ends on the date of the substantial completion, NOT the date of the final completion.

109. Answer:

If a contractor fails to pay one of his subcontractors, the owner can issue a **joint** **check** to the contractor and to the subcontractor who has not been paid by the contractor.

A **joint check** is a check made payable to two parties, and neither payee can cash or deposit the **joint check** without the endorsement or consent of the other.

110. Answer: b, c, and f

If asbestos or PCB or other hazardous materials are discovered at the concealed space of a project, the contractor:

- should stop the work at the affected area immediately
- is entitled to a change order.
- should proceed to mediation directly for disputes (Disputes related to hazardous materials should proceed to mediation directly. They are different from most other claims that are normally submitted to the architect for initial determination).

B. Mock Exam Answers and Explanations: Case Study

1. Major criteria, overall strategy and tips for the case study:

1) The building has one high roof and one low roof.
2) Outside edges of the roof planes must coincide with the dashed lines indicating the outermost edges of the roofs. Gutters and downspouts can be placed beyond with the dashed lines.
3) The slope for the roof over the Multi-purpose Room and Lobby shall be between 6:12 and 12:12.
4) The slope for the roof over the remaining spaces shall be between 2:12 and 5:12.
5) Check the elevations of the low points of upper roof and high points of the lower roof, and make sure you leave adequate space to accommodate the 1'-6" thick roof and structural assembly and the **2'-6" high clerestory window** in the west wall.
6) Provide skylights for rooms have no windows and no clerestory window.
7) Halls, storage rooms, or closets do not need skylights.
8) Check the elevations of the low points of the lower roof, and make sure you leave adequate space to accommodate the 1'-6" thick roof and structural assembly and the **8'-0" high first floor ceiling**.
9) Do NOT miss the gutters or downspouts.
10) Do NOT miss the plumbing vent stacks, and exhaust fan vents for the restrooms and the Break Room.
11) Do NOT miss the skylights at the Men's Restroom and the Women's Restroom.
12) Place the HVAC condensing unit on a roof with a slope of 5:12 or less, but NOT in front of the clerestory window.
13) Make sure the HVAC condensing unit has the required 3'-0" minimum clearance from all roof edges.

2. Mock Exam Answers and Explanations: Case Study

LEGEND:

HREL   HIGH ROOF ELEVATION
LREL   LOW ROOF ELEVATION

A/C   HVAC CONDENSING UNIT

⊚   VENT STACK

▨   EXHAUST FAN

▭   SKYLIGHT

▱   GUTTER

•   DOWNSPOUT

▨▨▨   FLASHING

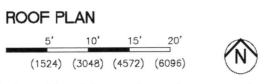

ROOF PLAN

Scale: 5' 10' 15' 20'
(1524) (3048) (4572) (6096)

Figure 4.13   Roof plan with minimum slopes for case study

111. Answer: See minimum slopes added in figure 4.13.

112. Answer: See minimum spot elevations added in figure 4.13.

Figure 3.43 provides the horizontal dimensions you need to calculate most spot elevations.

For the *low* roof:
Since the minimum ceiling height is 8'-0", and the total thickness for the roof and structural assembly is 18", the minimum spot elevation for the lowest points A & E = 8'-0" + 18" = 9'-6".

The distance between points D & E = (12'-5") + (10'-7") = 23', and the slope is 2 in per foot. So, the spot elevation at point D = (9'-6") + 23' x (2/12) = (9'-6") + (3'-10") = 13'-4".

The distance between points D & G (horizontally along the slope direction) = 10', and the slope is 2 in per foot.
So, the spot elevation at point G = (13'-4") + 10' x (2/12) = (13'-4") + (1'-8") = 15'-0".

For the *high* roof:
Per the program:
- The total thickness for the roof and structural assembly is 18".
- The Multi-Purpose Room has a 30-inch-high continuous horizontal clerestory window in the existing *east* wall.
- The clerestory sill is included in the overall height dimension.

So, the high roof at point D should be 18" + 30" = 4'-0" higher than the low roof.
The spot elevation at the *high* roof above point D = (13'-4") + (4'-0") = 17'-4", and the elevation for the entire eave of the high roof along the east wall should equal 17'-4" too.

Since the roof structure for the building is symmetrical, the spot elevation at point B is 17'-4".

The distance between points B & C (along the slope direction) = 10', and the slope is 6 in per foot.
So, the spot elevation at point C = (17'-4") + 10' x (6/12) = (17'-4") + (5'-0") = 22'-4".
The ridge continues at the same elevation of 22'-4" to point F.

113. Answer: See the skylights added on figure 4.13. The program requires skylights in all rooms that have no window or clerestory window except for storage rooms, closets, and halls. These are the Women's Restroom and the Break Room.

114. Answer: See the HVAC condensing unit added on figure 4.13. Placing the unit anywhere in the hatched area on the low roof is acceptable.

Per the program:
- You need to place the HVAC condensing unit on a roof with a slope of 5:12 or less. This means you can only place the unit on the *low* roof since its slope is 2:12 and the *high* roof slope is 6:12.
- Do not place the HVAC condensing unit in front of the clerestory window. This means it is safer to simply put the unit to the west of the roof ridge and to the south of the Multi-Purpose Room since the clerestory window is on the existing *east* wall of the Multi-Purpose Room.
- Maintain a minimum of 3'-0" clearance from all roof edges.

115. Answer: See two vent stacks added in figure 4.13. The vent stacks are added in the wall behind the sinks at the rest rooms and in the wall behind the sink at the kitchen.

116. Answer: See three exhaust fans added in figure 4.13. The exhaust fans are added in the ceiling near the toilets at the rest rooms and in the ceiling near the sink in the kitchen.

117. Answer: See the flashing added in figure 4.13 at the intersection of the chimney and the *high* roof, and at the intersection of the Multi-Purpose Room and the *low* roof.

118. Answer: See six gutters added in figure 4.13 along the east and west eaves of the *high* and *low* roofs.

119. Answer: See ten downspouts added in figure 4.13 at one or both ends of each gutter along the east and west eaves of the *high* and *low* roofs.

120. Answer: See *maximum* slopes, and the *updated minimum* spot elevations added in figure 4.14.

Figure 3.43 provides the horizontal dimensions you need to calculate most spot elevations.

For the *low* roof:
Since the minimum ceiling height is 8'-0", and the total thickness for the roof and structural assembly is 18", the minimum spot elevation for the lowest points A & E = 8'-0" + 18" = 9'-6".

The distance between points D & E = (12'-5") + (10'-7") = 23', and the slope is 5 in per foot. So, the spot elevation at point D = (9'-6") + 23' x (5/12) = (9'-6") + (9'-7") = 19'-1".

The distance between points D & G (horizontally along the slope direction) = 10', and the slope is 2 in per foot.
So, the spot elevation at point G = (19'-1") + 10' x (5/12) = (19'-1") + (4'-2") = 23'-3".

For the *high* roof:

Per the program:

- The total thickness for the roof and structural assembly is 18".
- The Multi-Purpose Room has a 30-inch-high continuous horizontal clerestory window in the existing *east* wall.
- The clerestory sill is included in the overall height dimension.

So, the *high* roof at point D should be 18" + 30" = 4'-0" higher than the *low* roof.

The spot elevation at the *high* roof above point D = (19'-1") + (4'-0") = 23'-1", and the elevation for the entire eave of the high roof along the east wall should equal 23'-1" too.

Since the roof structure for the building is symmetrical, the spot elevation at point B is 23'-1".

The distance between points B & C (along the slope direction) = 10', and the slope is 12 in per foot.

So, the spot elevation at point C = (23'-1") + 10' x (12/12) = (23'-1") + 10' = 33'-1".
The ridge continues at the same elevation of 33'-1" to point F.

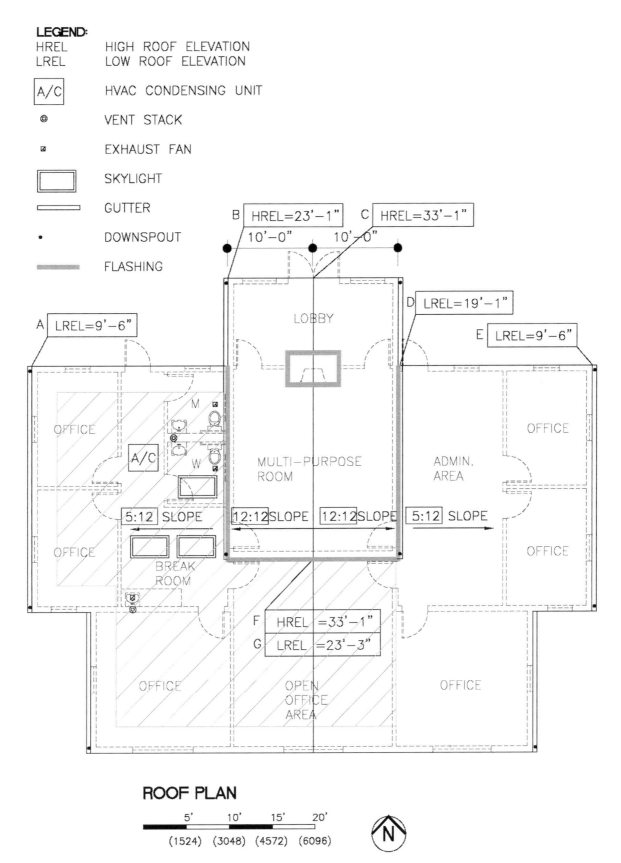

ROOF PLAN

5'   10'   15'   20'
(1524) (3048) (4572) (6096)

Figure 4.14   *Maximum* slopes and the *updated minimum* spot elevations

C. How We Came Up with the PDD Mock Exam Questions

We came up with all the PDD Mock Exam questions based on the ARE 5.0 Handbook, and we developed the Mock Exam based on the *five* weighted sections. See a detailed breakdown in the following table:

Note: *If the text on following table is too small for you to read, then you can go to our forum, sign up for a free account, and download the FREE 11x17 full size pdf format files for these tables at:*
GeeForum.com

Sections	Expected Number of Items	Actual Number of Items
Total	120	120
Section 1: Integration of Building Materials & Systems (31-37%)	**37-45**	**43**
• Analyze the integration of architectural systems and technologies to meet		6
• Determine the size of mechanical, electrical, and plumbing systems and components to meet project goals (U/A)		12
• Determine the size of structural systems to meet project goals (U/A)		7
• Integrate specialty systems such as acoustics, lighting, fire suppression, conveying, security, and communications to meet project goals (U/A)		4
• Determine how to detail the integration of multiple building systems and technologies (U/A)		7
• Coordinate mechanical, electrical, plumbing, structural, and specialty systems and technologies (U/A)		7
Section 2: Construction Documentation (32-38%)	**38-46**	**46**
• Determine appropriate documentation of building design (A/E)		22
• Determine appropriate documentation of site features (A/E)		4
• Determine appropriate documentation of detailed building drawings within individual architectural systems (A/E)		7
• Apply standards required to assemble a set of clear and coordinated construction documentation (U/A)		10
• Determine impact of project changes on documentation requirements and methods to communicate those changes to owner and design team (U/A)		3
Section 3: Project Manual & Specifications (12-18%)	**14-22**	**14**
• Identify and prioritize components required to write, maintain, and refine project manual (U/A)		6
• Identify and prioritize components required to write, maintain, and refine project specifications (U/A)		4
• Coordinate specifications with construction documentation (U/A)		4
Section 4: Codes & Regulations (8-14%)	**9-17**	**15**
• Determine adherence to building regulatory requirements (IBC) at detail level (U/A)		11
• Determine adherence with specialty regulatory requirements at the detail level (U/A)		4
Section 5: Construction Cost Estimates (2-8%)	**2-9**	**2**
• Analyze construction cost estimates to confirm alignment with project design (A/E)		2
Total	**120**	**120**

Appendixes

A. List of Figures

B. Official reference materials suggested by NCARB

1. Resources Available While Testing
Tips:
- *You need to read through these pages several times and become very familiar with them to save time in the real ARE exams.*

United States. American Institute of Steel Construction, Inc. *Steel Construction Manual*; 14th edition. Chicago, Illinois, 2011.

Beam Diagrams and Formulas:
- Simple Beam: Diagrams and Formulas - Conditions 1-3, page 3-213; Conditions 4-6, page 3-214; Conditions 7-9, page 3-215
- Beam Fixed at Both Ends: Diagrams and Formulas - Conditions 15-17, page 3-218
- Beam Overhanging One Support: Diagrams and Formulas - Conditions 24-28, pages 3-221 & 222

Dimensions and Properties:
- W Shapes 44 thru 27: Dimensions and Properties, pages 1-12 thru 17
- W Shapes 24 thru W14x145: Dimensions and Properties, pages 1-18 thru 23
- W Shapes 14x132 thru W4: Dimensions and Properties, pages 1-24 thru 29
- C Shapes: Dimensions and Properties, pages 1-36 & 37
- Angles: Properties, pages 1-42 thru 49
- Rectangular HSS: Dimensions and Properties, pages 1-74 thru 91
- Square HSS: Dimensions and Properties, pages 1-92 thru 95
- Round HSS: Dimensions and Properties, pages 1-96 thru 100

United States. International Code Council, Inc. *2012 International Building Code.* Country Club Hills, Illinois, 2011.

Live and Concentrated Loads:
- Uniform and Concentrated Loads: IBC Table 1607.1, pages 340-341

2. Typical Beam Nomenclature

The following typical beam nomenclature is excerpted from:
United States. American Institute of Steel Construction, Inc. *Steel Construction Manual*;
14th edition. Chicago, Illinois, 2011.

E	Modulus of Elasticity of steel at 29,000 ksi	V_2	Vertical shear at right reaction point, or to left of intermediate reaction of beam, kips
I	Moment of Inertia of beam, in^4	V_3	Vertical shear at right reaction point, or to right of intermediate reaction of beam, kips
L	Total length of beam between reaction point, ft	V_x	Vertical shear at distance x from end of beam, kips
M_{max}	Maximum moment, kip-in	W	Total load on beam, kips
M_1	Maximum moment in left section of beam, kip-in	A	Measured distance along beam, in
M_2	Maximum moment in right section of beam, kip-in	B	Measured distance along beam which may be greater or less than a, in
M_3	Maximum positive moment in beam with combined end moment conditions, kip-in	L	Total length of beam between reaction points, in
M_x	Maximum at distance x from end of beam, kip-in	W	Uniformly distributed load per unit of length, kips/in
P	Concentrated load, kips	w_1	Uniformly distributed load per unit of length nearest left reaction, kips/in
P_1	Concentrated load nearest left reaction, kips	w_2	Uniformly distributed load per unit of length nearest right reaction and of different magnitude than w1, kips/in
P_2	Concentrated load nearest right reaction and of different magnitude than P_1, kips	X	Any distance measured along beam from left reaction, in
R	End beam reaction for any condition of symmetrical loading, kips	x_1	Any distance measured along overhang section of beam from nearest reaction point, in
R_1	Left end beam reaction, kips	Δ_{max}	Maximum deflection, in
R_2	Right end or intermediate beam reaction, kips	Δa	Deflection at point of load, in
R_3	Right end beam reaction, kips	Δx	Deflection at point x distance from left reaction, in
V	Maximum vertical shear for any condition of symmetrical loading, kips	Δx_1	Deflection of overhang section of beam at any distance from nearest reaction point, in

V_1	Maximum vertical shear in left section of beam, kips		

3. Formulas Available While Testing
Tips:

- *These formulas and references will be available during the real exam. You should read through them a few times before the exam to become familiar with them. This will save you a lot of time during the real exam, and will help you solve structural calculations and other problems.*

Structural:
Flexural stress at extreme fiber
$$f = \frac{Mc}{I} = \frac{M}{S}$$

Flexural stress at any fiber
$$f = \frac{My}{I}$$

where y = distance from neutral axis to fiber

Average vertical shear
$$v = \frac{V}{A} = \frac{V}{dt}$$
for beams and girders

Horizontal shearing stress at any section A-A
$$v = \frac{VQ}{Ib}$$
where Q = statical moment about the neutral axis of the entire section of that portion of the cross-section lying outside of section A-A
b = width at section A-A

Electrical
$$Foot - candles = \frac{lumens}{area\ in\ ft^2}$$

$$Foot - candles = \frac{(lamp\ lumens)\ x\ (lamps\ per\ fixture)\ x\ (number\ of\ fixtures)\ x\ (CU)\ x\ (LLF)}{area\ in\ ft^2}$$

$$Number\ of\ luminaires = \frac{(foot - candles)\ x\ (floor\ area)}{(lumens)\ x\ (CU)\ x\ (LLF)}$$
where CU = coefficient of utilization
LLF = Light Loss Factor

$$DF_{AV} = 0.2x\frac{window\ area}{floor\ area}$$

for spaces with sidelighting or toplighting with vertical monitors

watts = volts x amperes x power factor
for AC circuits only

Demand charge = maximum power demand x demand tariff

Plumbing
$1\ psi = 2.31\ feet\ of\ water$

$1\ cubic\ foot = 7.5\ U.S.\ gallons$

HVAC

$$\frac{BTU}{year} = peak\ heat\ loss\ x\ \frac{full-load\ hours}{year}$$

$$\frac{\$}{year} = \frac{BTU}{year} \times \frac{fuel\ cost}{fuel\ heat\ value} \times efficiency$$

$BTU/h = (cfm)\ x\ (1.08)\ x\ (\Delta T)$

$1\ kWh = 3,400\ BTU/h$

$1\ ton\ of\ air\ conditioning = 12,000\ BTU/h$

$BTU/h = (U)\ x\ (A)\ x\ (T_d)$ *where Td is the difference between indoor and outdoor temperatures*

$U = 1/R_t$

$$U_o = \frac{(U_w \times A_w) + (U_{op} \times A_{op})}{Ao}$$

where o = total wall, w = window, and op = opaque wall

$$U_o = \frac{(U_R \times A_R) + (U_S \times A_S)}{Ao}$$

where o = total roof, R = roof, and S = skylight

$$R = x/k$$

where x = thickness of material in inches

$$Heat\ required = \frac{BTU/h}{temperature\ differential} \times (24\ hours) \times (DD\ °F)$$

where DD = degree days

Acoustics

$$\lambda = \frac{c}{f}$$

where λ = wavelength of sound (ft)
c = velocity of sound (fps)
f = frequency of sound (Hz)

$$a = SAC\ x\ S$$

where a = Absorption of a material used in space (sabins)
SAC = Sound Absorption Coefficient of the material
S = Exposed surface area of the material (ft^2)

$$A = \Sigma a$$

Where A = Total sound absorption of a room (sabins)
$\Sigma a = (S_1\ x\ SAC_1) + (S_2\ x\ SAC_2) + ...$

$$T = 0.05 \times \frac{V}{A}$$

where T = Reverberation time (seconds)
V = Volume of space (ft^3)

$$NRC = average\ SAC\ for\ frequency\ bands\ 250, 500, 1000, and\ 2000\ Hz$$

4. Common Abbreviations

Tips:

- *You need to read through these common abbreviations several times and become very familiar with them to save time in the real ARE exams.*

Professional Organizations, Societies, and Agencies

American Concrete Institute	ACI
American Institute of Architects	AIA
American Institute of Steel Construction	AISC
American National Standards Institute	ANSI
American Society for Testing and Materials	ASTM
American Society of Civil Engineers	ASCE
American Society of Heating, Refrigerating, and Air-Conditioning Engineers	ASHRAE
American Society of Mechanical Engineers	ASME
American Society of Plumbing Engineers	ASPE
Architectural Woodwork Institute	AWI
Construction Specifications Institute	CSI
Department of Housing and Urban Development	HUD
Environmental Protection Agency	EPA
Federal Emergency Management Agency	FEMA
National Fire Protection Association	NFPA
Occupational Safety and Health Administration	OSHA
U.S. Green Building Council	USGBC

Tips:

- *You need to look through the following codes and regulations & AIA contract documents several times and become very familiar with them to save time in the real ARE exams. Read some of the important sections in details.*

AIA Contract Documents

A101-2007, Standard Form of Agreement Between Owner and Contractor - Stipulated Sum	A101
A201-2007, General Conditions of the Contract for Construction	A201
A305-1986, Contractor's Qualification Statement	A305
A701-1997, Instructions to Bidders	A701
B101-2007, Standard Form of Agreement Between Owner and Architect	B101
C401-2007, Standard Form of Agreement Between Architect and Consultant	C401
G701-2001, Change Order	G701
G702-1992, Application and Certificate for Payment	G702
G703-1992, Continuation Sheet	G703
G704-2000, Certificate of Substantial Completion	G704

Codes and Regulations

ADA Standards for Accessible Design	ADA

International Code Council	ICC
International Building Code	IBC
International Energy Conservation Code	IECC
International Existing Building Code	IEBC
International Mechanical Code	IMC
International Plumbing Code	IPC
International Residential Code	IRC
Leadership in Energy and Environmental Design	LEED
National Electrical Code	NEC

Commonly Used Terms

Air Handling Unit	AHU
Authority Having Jurisdiction	AHJ
Building Information Modeling	BIM
Concrete Masonry Unit	CMU
Contract Administration	CA
Construction Document	CD
Dead Load	DL
Design Development	DD
Exterior Insulation and Finish System	EIFS
Furniture, Furnishings & Equipment	FF&E
Floor Area Ratio	FAR
Heating, Ventilating, and Air Conditioning	HVAC
Insulating Glass Unit	IGU
Indoor Air Quality	IAQ
Indoor Environmental Quality	IEQ
Live Load	LL
Material Safety Data Sheets	MSDS
Photovoltaic	PV
Reflected Ceiling Plan	RCP
Schematic Design	SD
Variable Air Volume	VAV
Volatile Organic Compound	VOC
British Thermal Unit	btu
Cubic Feet per Minute	cfm
Cubic Feet per Second	cfs
Cubic Foot	cu. ft. ft^3
Cubic Inch	cu. in. in^3
Cubic Yard	cu. yd. yd^3
Decibel	dB
Foot	ft
Foot-candle	fc
Gross Square Feet	gsf

Impact Insulation Class	IIC
Inch	in
Net Square Feet	nsf
Noise Reduction Coefficient	NRC
Pound	lb
Pounds per Linear Foot	plf
Pounds per Square Foot	psf
Pounds per Square Inch	psi
Sound Transmission Class	STC
Square Foot	sq. ft.
	sf
	ft^2
Square Inch	sq. in.
	in^2
Square Yard	sq. yd.

5. **General NCARB reference materials for ARE:**

Per NCARB, all candidates should become familiar with the latest version of the following codes:

International Code Council, Inc. (ICC)
International Building Code
International Mechanical Code
International Plumbing Code

National Fire Protection Association (NFPA)
Life Safety Code (NFPA 101)
National Electrical Code (NFPA 70)

National Research Council of Canada
National Building Code of Canada
National Plumbing Code of Canada
National Fire Code of Canada

American Institute of Architects
AIA Documents - 2007

6. Official NCARB reference materials matrix

Per NCARB, all candidates should become familiar with the latest version of the following:

Reference	PcM	PjM	PA	PPD	PDD	CE
2009 ASHRAE Handbook: Fundamentals, I-P Edition. ASHRAE, 2009				■	■	
2010 ADA Standards for Accessible Design U.S. Department of Justice, 2010			■	■		
The American Institute of Architects Official Guide to the 2007 AIA Contract Documents. The American Institute of Architects. John Wiley & Sons, 2009	■	■				■
The Architect's Guide to Small Firm Management: Making Chaos Work for Your Small Firm. Rena M. Klein, FAIA. The American Institute of Architects. John Wiley & Sons, 2010	■					
The Architect's Handbook of Professional Practice The American Institute of Architects John Wiley & Sons, latest edition	■	■		■		
Architectural Acoustics. M. David Egan. J. Ross Publishing, 2007. Reprint. Original publication McGraw Hill, 1988				■		
Architectural Graphic Standards The American Institute of Architects John Wiley & Sons, latest edition				■	■	
Architectural Graphic Standards for Residential Construction The American Institute of Architects John Wiley & Sons, latest edition				■	■	
BIM and Integrated Design: Strategies for Architectural Practice Randy Deutsch, AIA, LEED-AP The American Institute of Architects John Wiley & Sons, 2011	■	■				
Building Codes Illustrated: A Guide to Understanding the 2012 International Building Code. Francis D.K. Ching and Steven R. Winkel, FAIA, PE. John Wiley & Sons, 2012			■	■	■	
Building Construction Illustrated Francis D. K. Ching John Wiley & Sons, latest edition				■	■	
Building Structures James Ambrose and Patrick Tripeny John Wiley & Sons, 3rd edition, 2012				■	■	

Reference	PcM	PjM	PA	PPD	PDD	CE
Code of Ethics and Professional Conduct AIA Office of General Counsel. The American Institute of Architects, latest edition	▓					
CSI MasterFormat. The Construction Specifications Institute. 2004 edition						▓
Dictionary of Architecture and Construction. Cyril M. Harris. McGraw-Hill, 4th edition, 2006				▓	▓	▓
Fundamentals of Building Construction: Materials and Methods Edward Allen and Joseph Iano John Wiley & Sons, latest edition				▓		▓
Heating, Cooling, Lighting: Sustainable Design Methods for Architects. Norbert Lechner. John Wiley & Sons, 3rd edition, 2008				▓		
The HOK Guidebook to Sustainable Design Sandra F. Mendler, William Odell, and Mary Ann Lazarus John Wiley & Sons, 2nd edition, 2006				▓		
ICC A117.1-2009 Accessible and Usable Buildings and Facilities International Code Council, 2010			▓			
International Building Code (2012) International Code Council, 2011			▓	▓		
Landscape Architectural Graphic Standards. Leonard J. Hopper, Editor. John Wiley & Sons, 2007				▓		
Law for Architects: What You Need to Know. Robert F. Herrmann and the Attorneys at Menaker & Herrmann LLP. W. W. Norton, 2012	▓					
Mechanical & Electrical Equipment for Buildings. Walter T. Grondzik, Alison G. Kwok, Benjamin Stein, and John S. Reynolds, Editors. John Wiley & Sons, latest edition				▓	▓	
Mechanical and Electrical Systems in Buildings. Richard R. Janis and William K. Y. Tao. Prentice Hall, latest edition.				▓	▓	
Minimum Design Loads for Buildings and Other Structures (7-10) American Society of Civil Engineers, 2013					▓	
Olin's Construction Principles, Materials, and Methods. H. Leslie Simmons. John Wiley & Sons, latest edition				▓	▓	

Reference	PcM	PjM	PA	PPD	PDD	CE
Planning and Urban Design Standards American Planning Association John Wiley & Sons, 2006			■			
Plumbing, Electricity, Acoustics: Sustainable Design Methods for Architecture. Norbert Lechner. John Wiley & Sons, 2012				■	■	
Problem Seeking: An Architectural Programming Primer William M. Peña and Steven A. Parshall John Wiley & Sons, latest edition			■			
Professional Practice: A Guide to Turning Designs into Buildings. Paul Segal, FAIA. W. W. Norton, 2006	■	■	■			
The Professional Practice of Architectural Working Drawings. Osamu A. Wakita, Nagy R. Bakhoum, and Richard M. Linde. John Wiley & Sons, 4th edition, 2012					■	
The Project Resource Manual: CSI Manual of Practice. The Construction Specifications Institute. McGraw-Hill, 5th edition, 2005						■
Rules of Conduct National Council of Architectural Registration Boards, latest edition	■					
Simplified Engineering for Architects and Builders James Ambrose and Patrick Tripeny John Wiley & Sons, latest edition					■	
Site Engineering for Landscape Architects Steven Strom, Kurt Nathan, and Jake Woland, Editors. John Wiley & Sons, 2013				■		
Site Planning and Design Handbook Thomas H. Russ McGraw-Hill, 2nd edition, 2009			■	■		
Space Planning Basics Mark Karlen and Rob Fleming John Wiley & Sons, latest edition			■			
Steel Construction Manual American Institute of Steel Construction Ingram, latest edition					■	
Structural Design: A Practical Guide for Architects James R. Underwood and Michele Chiuini John Wiley & Sons, 2nd edition, 2007				■	■	

Reference	PcM	PjM	PA	PPD	PDD	CE
Structures Daniel Schodek and Martin Bechthold Pearson/Prentice Hall, latest edition				▓	▓	
Sun, Wind, and Light: Architectural Design Strategies G.Z. Brown and Mark DeKay John Wiley & Sons, 2nd edition, 2001				▓		
Sustainable Construction: Green Building Design and Delivery Charles J. Kibert. John Wiley & Sons, 2005				▓		
Time-Saver Standards for Architectural Design: Technical Data for Professional Practice Donald Watson and Michael J. Crosbie, Editors. McGraw-Hill, 8th edition, 2004				▓	▓	
A Visual Dictionary of Architecture Francis D.K. Ching John Wiley & Sons, latest edition				▓	▓	

The following AIA Contract Documents have content covered in the of ARE 5.0 exams. Candidates can access them for free through their NCARB Record.

Conventional Family	PcM	PjM	PA	PPD	PDD	CE
A101-2007, Standard Form of Agreement Between Owner and Contractor where the basis of payment is a Stipulated Sum						▓
A201-2007, General Conditions of the Contract for Construction		▓				▓
A701-1997, Instructions to Bidders		▓				▓
B101-2007, Standard Form of Agreement Between Owner and Architect	▓	▓				
C401-2007, Standard Form of Agreement Between Architect and Consultant	▓	▓				▓

Contract Administration and Project Management Forms	PcM	PjM	PA	PPD	PDD	CE
A305-1986, Contractor's Qualification Statement						▓
G701-2001, Change Order						▓
G702-1992, Application and Certificate for Payment						▓
G703-1992, Continuation Sheet						▓
G704-2000, Certificate of Substantial Completion						▓

7. Extra study materials

The following are some extra study materials if you have some additional time and want to learn more. If you are tight on time, you can simply look through them and focus on the sections that cover your weakness:

ACI Code 318-05 (Building Code Requirements for Reinforced Concrete)
American Concrete Institute, 2005

OR
CAN/CSA-A23.1-94 (Concrete Materials and Methods of Concrete Construction) and CAN/CSA-A23.3-94 (Design of Concrete Structures for Buildings)
Canadian Standards Association

Design Value for Wood Construction
American Wood Council, 2005

Elementary Structures for Architects and Builders, Fourth Edition
Ronald E. Shaeffer
Prentice Hall, 2006

Introduction to Wood Design
Canadian Wood Council, 2005

Manual of Steel Construction: Allowable Stress Design; 9th Edition.
American Institute of Steel Construction, Inc. Chicago, Illinois, 1989

National Building Code of Canada, 2005
Parts 1, 3, 4, 9; Appendix A
Supplement
Chapters 1, 2, 4; Commentaries A, D, F, H, I

NEHRP (National Earthquake Hazards Reduction Program) Recommended Provisions for Seismic Regulations for New Buildings and Other Structures Parts 1 and 2
FEMA 2003

Simplified Building Design for Wind and Earthquake Forces
James Ambrose and Dimitry Vergun
John Wiley & Sons, 1997

Simplified Design of Concrete Structures,
Eighth Edition
James Ambrose, Patrick Tripeny
John Wiley & Sons, 2007

Simplified Design of Masonry Structures

James Ambrose
John Wiley & Sons, 1997

Simplified Design of Steel Structures, Eighth Edition
James Ambrose, Patrick Tripeny
John Wiley & Sons, 2007

Simplified Design of Wood Structures, Fifth Edition
James Ambrose
John Wiley & Sons, 2009

Simplified Mechanics and Strength of Materials, Fifth Edition
Harry Parker and James Ambrose
John Wiley & Sons, 2002

Standard Specifications Load Tables &Weight Tables for Steel Joists and Joist Girders
Steel Joist Institute, latest edition

Steel Construction Manual, Latest edition
American Institute of Steel Construction, 2006

OR
Handbook of Steel Construction, Latest edition; and *CAN/CSA-S16-01 and CISC Commentary*
Canadian Institute of Steel Construction

Steel Deck Institute Tables
Steel Deck Institute

OR
LSD Steel Deck Tables
Caradon Metal Building Products

Structural Concepts and Systems for Architects and Engineers, Second Edition
T.Y. Lin and Sidney D. Stotesbury
Van Nostrand Reinhold, 1988

Structural Design: A Practical Guide for Architects
James Underwood and Michele Chiuini
John Wiley & Sons, latest edition

Structure in Architecture: The Building of Buildings
Mario Salvadori with Robert Heller
Prentice-Hall, 1986

Understanding Structures
Fuller Moore
McGraw-Hill, 1999

Wood Design Manual and *CAN/CSA-086.1-94 and Commentary*
Canadian Wood Council

C. Other reference materials

Chen, Gang. *Building Construction: Project Management, Construction Administration, Drawings, Specs, Detailing Tips, Schedules, Checklists, and Secrets Others Don't Tell You (Architectural Practice Simplified, 2nd edition).* ArchiteG, Inc., A good introduction to the architectural practice and construction documents and service, including discussions of MasterSpec format and specification sections.

Chen, Gang. ***LEED v4 Green Associate Exam Guide (LEED GA):*** *Comprehensive Study Materials, Sample Questions, Mock Exam, Green Building LEED Certification, and Sustainability*, Book 2, LEED Exam Guide series, ArchiteG.com, the latest edition. ArchiteG, Inc. Latest Edition. This is a very comprehensive and concise book on the LEED Green Associate Exam. Some readers have passed the LEED Green Associate Exam by studying this book for 10 hours.

Ching, Francis. *Architecture: Form, Space, & Order.* Wiley, latest edition. It is one of the best architectural books that you can have. I still flip through it every now and then. It is a great book for inspiration.

Frampton, Kenneth. *Modern Architecture: A Critical History.* Thames and Hudson, London, latest edition. A valuable resource for architectural history.

Jarzombek, Mark M. (Author), Vikramaditya Prakash (Author), Francis D. K. Ching (Editor). *A Global History of Architecture.* Wiley, latest edition. A valuable and comprehensive resource for architectural history with 1000 b & w photos, 50 color photos, and 1500 b & w illustrations. It doesn't limit the topic on a Western perspective, but rather through a global vision.

Trachtenberg, Marvin and Isabelle Hyman. *Architecture: From Pre-history to Post-Modernism.* Prentice Hall, Englewood Cliffs, NJ latest edition. A valuable and comprehensive resource for architectural history.

D. Some Important Information about Architects and the Profession of Architecture

What Architects Do?

Architects plan and design houses, factories, office buildings, and other structures.

Duties
Architects typically do the following:

- Meet with clients to determine objectives and requirements for structures
- Give preliminary estimates on cost and construction time
- Prepare structure specifications
- Direct workers who prepare drawings and documents
- Prepare scaled drawings, either with computer software or by hand
- Prepare contract documents for building contractors
- Manage construction contracts
- Visit worksites to ensure that construction adheres to architectural plans
- Seek new work by marketing and giving presentations

People need places to live, work, play, learn, shop, and eat. Architects are responsible for designing these places. They work on public or private projects and design both indoor and outdoor spaces. Architects can be commissioned to design anything from a single room to an entire complex of buildings.

Architects discuss the objectives, requirements, and budget of a project with clients. In some cases, architects provide various predesign services, such as feasibility and environmental impact studies, site selection, cost analyses, and design requirements.

Architects develop final construction plans after discussing and agreeing on the initial proposal with clients. These plans show the building's appearance and details of its construction. Accompanying these plans are drawings of the structural system; air-conditioning, heating, and ventilating systems; electrical systems; communications systems; and plumbing. Sometimes, landscape plans are included as well. In developing designs, architects must follow state and local building codes, zoning laws, fire regulations, and other ordinances, such as those requiring easy access to buildings for people who are disabled.

Computer-aided design and drafting (CADD) and building information modeling (BIM) have replaced traditional drafting paper and pencil as the most common methods for creating designs and construction drawings. However, hand-drawing skills are still required, especially during the conceptual stages of a project and when an architect is at a construction site.

As construction continues, architects may visit building sites to ensure that contractors follow the design, adhere to the schedule, use the specified materials, and meet work-quality standards. The job is not complete until all construction is finished, required tests are conducted, and construction costs are paid.

Architects may also help clients get construction bids, select contractors, and negotiate construction contracts.

Architects often collaborate with workers in related occupations, such as civil engineers, urban and regional planners, drafters, interior designers, and landscape architects.

Work Environment
Although architects usually work in an office, they must also travel to construction sites.

Architects held about 112,600 jobs in 2014, with 69 percent employed in architectural, engineering, and related services. About 1 in 5 were self-employed.

Architects spend much of their time in offices, where they meet with clients, develop reports and drawings, and work with other architects and engineers. They also visit construction sites to ensure clients' objectives are met and to review the progress of projects. Some architects work from home offices.

Work Schedules
Most architects work full time and many work additional hours, especially when facing deadlines. Self-employed architects may have more flexible work schedules.

How to Become an Architect
There are typically three main steps to becoming a licensed architect: completing a professional degree in architecture, gaining relevant experience through a paid internship, and passing the Architect Registration Examination.

Education
In all states, earning a professional degree in architecture is typically the first step to becoming an architect. Most architects earn their professional degree through a 5-year Bachelor of Architecture degree program, intended for students with no previous architectural training. Many earn a master's degree in architecture, which can take 1 to 5 years in addition to the time spent earning a bachelor's degree. The amount of time required depends on the extent of the student's previous education and training in architecture.

A typical bachelor's degree program includes courses in architectural history and theory, building design with an emphasis on computer-aided design and drafting (CADD), structures, construction methods, professional practices, math, physical sciences, and liberal arts. Central to most architectural programs is the design studio, where students apply the skills and concepts learned in the classroom to create drawings and three-dimensional models of their designs.

Currently, 34 states require that architects hold a professional degree in architecture from one of the 123 schools of architecture accredited by the National Architectural Accrediting Board (NAAB). State licensing requirements can be found at the National Council of Architectural Registration Boards (NCARB). In the states that do not have that requirement, applicants can become licensed with 8 to 13 years of related work experience in addition to a high school diploma. However, most architects in these states still obtain a professional degree in architecture.

Training

All state architectural registration boards require architecture graduates to complete a lengthy paid internship—generally 3 years of experience—before they may sit for the Architect Registration Examination. Most new graduates complete their training period by working at architectural firms through the Intern Development Program (IDP), a program run by NCARB that guides students through the internship process. Some states allow a portion of the training to occur in the offices of employers in related careers, such as engineers and general contractors. Architecture students who complete internships while still in school can count some of that time toward the 3-year training period.

Interns in architectural firms may help design part of a project. They may help prepare architectural documents and drawings, build models, and prepare construction drawings on CADD. Interns may also research building codes and write specifications for building materials, installation criteria, the quality of finishes, and other related details. Licensed architects will take the documents that interns produce, make edits to them, finalize plans, and then sign and seal the documents.

Licenses, Certifications, and Registrations

All states and the District of Columbia require architects to be licensed. Licensing requirements typically include completing a professional degree in architecture, gaining relevant experience through a paid internship, and passing the Architect Registration Examination.

Most states also require some form of continuing education to keep a license, and some additional states are expected to adopt mandatory continuing education. Requirements vary by state but usually involve additional education through workshops, university classes, conferences, self-study courses, or other sources.

A growing number of architects voluntarily seek certification from NCARB. This certification makes it easier to become licensed across states, because it is the primary requirement for reciprocity of licensing among state boards that are NCARB members. In 2014, approximately one-third of all licensed architects had the certification.

Advancement

After many years of work experience, some architects advance to become architectural and engineering managers. These managers typically coordinate the activities of employees and may work on larger construction projects.

Important Qualities

Analytical skills. Architects must understand the content of designs and the context in which they were created. For example, architects must understand the locations of mechanical systems and how those systems affect building operations.

Communication skills. Architects share their ideas, both in oral presentations and in writing, with clients, other architects, and workers who help prepare drawings. Many also give presentations to explain their ideas and designs.

Creativity. Architects design the overall look of houses, buildings, and other structures. Therefore, the final product should be attractive and functional.

Organizational skills. Architects often manage contracts. Therefore, they must keep records related to the details of a project, including total cost, materials used, and progress.

Technical skills. Architects need to use CADD technology to create plans as part of building information modeling (BIM).

Visualization skills. Architects must be able to see how the parts of a structure relate to each other. They also must be able to visualize how the overall building will look once completed.

Pay
The median annual wage for architects was $76,100 in May 2015. The median wage is the wage at which half the workers in an occupation earned more than that amount and half earned less. The lowest 10 percent earned less than $46,080, and the highest 10 percent earned more than $125,520.

Some firms pay tuition and fees toward continuing education requirements for their employees. Most architects work full time and many work additional hours, especially when facing deadlines. Self-employed architects may have more flexible work hours.

Job Outlook
Employment of architects is projected to grow 7 percent from 2014 to 2024, about as fast as the average for all occupations.

Architects will be needed to make plans and designs for the construction and renovation of homes, offices, retail stores, and other structures. Many school districts and universities are expected to build new facilities or renovate existing ones. In addition, demand is expected for more healthcare facilities as the baby-boomer population ages and as more individuals use healthcare services. The construction of new retail establishments may also require more architects.

Demand is projected for architects with a knowledge of "green design," also called sustainable design. Sustainable design emphasizes the efficient use of resources, such as energy and water conservation; waste and pollution reduction; and environmentally friendly design, specifications, and materials. Rising energy costs and increased concern about the environment have led to many new buildings being built with more sustainable designs.

The use of CADD and, more recently, BIM, has made architects more productive. These technologies have allowed architects to do more work without the help of drafters while making it easier to share the work with engineers, contractors, and clients.

Job Prospects

With a high number of students graduating with degrees in architecture, very strong competition for internships and jobs is expected. Competition for jobs will be especially strong at the most prestigious architectural firms. Those with up-to-date technical skills—including a strong grasp of CADD and BIM—and experience in sustainable design will have an advantage.

Employment of architects is strongly tied to the activity of the construction industry. Therefore, these workers may experience periods of unemployment when there is a slowdown in requests for new projects or when the overall level of construction falls.

State & Area Data

Occupational Employment Statistics (OES)

The Occupational Employment Statistics (OES) program produces employment and wage estimates annually for over 800 occupations. These estimates are available for the nation as a whole, for individual states, and for metropolitan and nonmetropolitan areas. The link(s) below go to OES data maps for employment and wages by state and area.
https://www.bls.gov/oes/current/oes171011.htm#st

Projections Central

Occupational employment projections are developed for all states by Labor Market Information (LMI) or individual state Employment Projections offices. All state projections data are available at www.projectionscentral.com. Information on this site allows projected employment growth for an occupation to be compared among states or to be compared within one state. In addition, states may produce projections for areas; there are links to each state's websites where these data may be retrieved.

Career InfoNet

America's Career InfoNet includes hundreds of occupational profiles with data available by state and metro area. There are links in the left-hand side menu to compare occupational employment by state and occupational wages by local area or metro area. There is also a salary info tool to search for wages by zip code.

Related Occupations

Architects design buildings and related structures. Construction managers, like architects, also plan and coordinate activities concerned with the construction and maintenance of buildings and facilities. Others who engage in similar work are landscape architects, civil engineers, urban and regional planners, and designers, including interior designers, commercial and industrial designers, and graphic designers.

Sources of Additional Information

Disclaimer:

Links to non-BLS Internet sites are provided for your convenience and do not constitute an endorsement.

Information about education and careers in architecture can be obtained from:

- The American Institute of Architects, 1735 New York Ave. NW., Washington, DC 20006. Internet: http://www.aia.org
- National Architectural Accrediting Board: http://www.naab.org/
- National Council of Architectural Registration Boards, Suite 1100K, 1801 K St. NW., Washington, D.C. 20006. Internet: http://www.ncarb.org
  OOH ONET Codes 17-1011.00"

Source: Bureau of Labor Statistics, U.S. Department of Labor, *Occupational Outlook Handbook, 2016-17 Edition*, Architects, on the Internet at https://www.bls.gov/ooh/architecture-and-engineering/architects.htm (visited **January 26, 2017**).

Publish Date: Thursday, December 17, 2015

Note: Please check the website above for the latest information.

E. AIA Compensation Survey

Every 3 years, AIA publishes a Compensation Survey for various positions at architectural firms across the country. It is a good idea to find out the salary before you make the final decision to become an architect. If you are already an architect, it is also a good idea to determine if you are underpaid or overpaid.

See following link for some sample pages for the 2015 AIA Compensation Survey:

https://www.aia.org/resources/8066-aia-compensation-report

F. So ... You would Like to Study Architecture

To study architecture, you need to learn how to draft, how to understand and organize spaces and the interactions between interior and exterior spaces, how to do design, and how to communicate effectively. You also need to understand the history of architecture.

As an architect, a leader for a team of various design professionals, you not only need to know architecture, but also need to understand enough of your consultants' work to be able to coordinate them. Your consultants include soils and civil engineers, landscape architects, structural, electrical, mechanical, and plumbing engineers, interior designers, sign consultants, etc.

There are two major career paths for you in architecture: practice as an architect or teach in colleges or universities. The earlier you determine which path you are going to take, the more likely you will be successful at an early age. Some famous and well-respected architects, like my USC alumnus Frank Gehry, have combined the two paths successfully. They teach at the universities and have their own architectural practice. Even as a college or university professor, people respect you more if you have actual working experience and have some built projects. If you only teach in colleges or universities but have no actual working experience and have no built projects, people will consider you as a "paper" architect, and they are not likely to take you seriously, because they will think you probably do not know how to put a real building together.

In the U.S., if you want to practice architecture, you need to obtain an architect's license. It requires a combination of passing scores on the Architectural Registration Exam (ARE) and 8 years of education and/or qualified working experience, including at least 1 year of working experience in the U.S. Your working experience needs to be under the supervision of a licensed architect to be counted as qualified working experience for your architect's license.

If you work for a landscape architect or civil engineer or structural engineer, some states' architectural licensing boards will count your experience at a discounted rate for the qualification of your architect's license. For example, 2 years of experience working for a civil engineer may be counted as 1 year of qualified experience for your architect's license. You need to contact your state's architectural licensing board for specific licensing requirements for your state.

If you want to teach in colleges or universities, you probably want to obtain a master's degree or a Ph.D. It is not very common for people in the architectural field to have a Ph.D. One reason is that there are few Ph.D. programs for architecture. Another reason is that architecture is considered a profession and requires a license. Many people think an architect's license is more important than a Ph.D. degree. In many states, you need to have an architect's license to even use the title "architect," or the terms "architectural" or "architecture" to advertise your service. You cannot call yourself an architect if you do not have an architect's license, even if you have a Ph.D. in architecture. Violation of these rules brings punishment.

To become a tenured professor, you need to have a certain number of publications and pass the evaluation for the tenure position. Publications are very important for tenure track positions. Some people say for the tenured track positions in universities and colleges, it is "publish or perish."

The American Institute of Architects (AIA) is the national organization for the architectural profession. Membership is voluntary. There are different levels of AIA membership. Only licensed architects can be (full) AIA members. If you are an architectural student or an intern but not a licensed architect yet, you can join as an associate AIA member. Contact AIA for detailed information.

The National Council of Architectural Registration Boards (NCARB) is a nonprofit federation of architectural licensing boards. It has some very useful programs, such as IDP, to assist you in obtaining your architect's license. Contact NCARB for detailed information.

Back Page Promotion

You may be interested in some other books written by Gang Chen:

A. **ARE Mock Exam series. See the following link:**
   http://www.GreenExamEducation.com

B. **LEED Exam Guides series. See the following link:**
   http://www.GreenExamEducation.com

C. ***Building Construction:*** *Project Management, Construction Administration, Drawings, Specs, Detailing Tips, Schedules, Checklists, and Secrets Others Don't Tell You (Architectural Practice Simplified, 2nd edition)*
   http://www.GreenExamEducation.com

D. ***Planting Design Illustrated***
   http://www.GreenExamEducation.com

ARE Mock Exam Series

Published ARE books (One Mock Exam book for each ARE division, plus California Supplemental Mock Exam):

ARE 5.0 Mock Exam Series
Project Planning & Design (PPD) ARE 5.0 Mock Exam (Architect Registration Examination): ARE 5.0 Overview, Exam Prep Tips, Hot Spots, Case Studies, Drag-and-Place, Solutions and Explanations. **ISBN:** 9781612650296

Other books in the ARE 5.0 Mock Exam Series are being produced. Our goal is to produce one mock exam book PLUS one guidebook for each of the ARE 5.0 exam divisions.

ARE 4.0 Mock Exam Series
Programming, Planning & Practice (PPP) ARE Mock Exam (Architect Registration Examination): ARE Overview, Exam Prep Tips, Multiple-Choice Questions and Graphic Vignettes, Solutions and Explanations. **ISBN-13:** 9781612650067

Site Planning & Design ARE Mock Exam (SPD of Architect Registration Examination): ARE Overview, Exam Prep Tips, Multiple-Choice Questions and Graphic Vignettes, Solutions and Explanations. **ISBN-13:** 9781612650111

Building Design and Construction Systems (BDCS) ARE Mock Exam (Architect Registration Examination): ARE Overview, Exam Prep Tips, Multiple-Choice Questions and Graphic Vignettes, Solutions and Explanations. **ISBN-13:** 9781612650029

Schematic Design (SD) ARE Mock Exam (Architect Registration Examination): ARE Overview, Exam Prep Tips, Graphic Vignettes, Solutions and Explanations
ISBN: 9781612650050

Structural Systems ARE Mock Exam (SS of Architect Registration Examination): ARE Overview, Exam Prep Tips, Multiple-Choice Questions and Graphic Vignettes, Solutions and Explanations. **ISBN:** 9781612650012

Building Systems (BS) ARE Mock Exam (Architect Registration Examination): ARE Overview, Exam Prep Tips, Multiple-Choice Questions and Graphic Vignettes, Solutions and Explanations. **ISBN-13:** 9781612650036

Construction Documents and Service (CDS) Are Mock Exam (Architect Registration Examination): ARE Overview, Exam Prep Tips, Multiple-Choice Questions and Graphic Vignettes, Solutions and Explanations. **ISBN-13:** 9781612650005

Mock California Supplemental Exam (CSE of Architect Registration Examination): CSE Overview, Exam Prep Tips, General Section and Project Scenario Section, Questions, Solutions and Explanations. **ISBN:** 9781612650159

Upcoming ARE books:

Other books in the ARE Mock Exam Series are being produced. Our goal is to produce one mock exam book PLUS one guidebook for each of the ARE exam divisions.

See the following link for the latest information:
http://www.GreenExamEducation.com

LEED Exam Guides series
Comprehensive Study Materials, Sample Questions, Mock Exam, Building LEED Certification and Going Green

LEED (Leadership in Energy and Environmental Design) is the most important trend of development, and it is revolutionizing the construction industry. It has gained tremendous momentum and has a profound impact on our environment.

From LEED Exam Guides series, you will learn how to

1. Pass the LEED Green Associate Exam and various LEED AP + exams (each book will help you with a specific LEED exam).

2. Register and certify a building for LEED certification.

3. Understand the intent for each LEED prerequisite and credit.

4. Calculate points for a LEED credit.

5. Identify the responsible party for each prerequisite and credit.

6. Earn extra credit (exemplary performance) for LEED.

7. Implement the local codes and building standards for prerequisites and credit.

8. Receive points for categories not yet clearly defined by USGBC.

There is currently NO official book on the LEED Green Associate Exam, and most of the existing books on LEED and LEED AP are too expensive and too complicated to be practical and helpful. The pocket guides in LEED Exam Guides series fill in the blanks, demystify LEED, and uncover the tips, codes, and jargon for LEED as well as the true meaning of "going green." They will set up a solid foundation and fundamental framework of LEED for you. Each book in the LEED Exam Guides series covers every aspect of one or more specific LEED rating system(s) in plain and concise language and makes this information understandable to all people.

These pocket guides are small and easy to carry around. You can read them whenever you have a few extra minutes. They are indispensable books for all people—administrators; developers; contractors; architects; landscape architects; civil, mechanical, electrical, and plumbing engineers; interns; drafters; designers; and other design professionals.

Why is the LEED Exam Guides series needed?

A number of books are available that you can use to prepare for the LEED exams:

1. *USGBC Reference Guides.* You need to select the correct version of the *Reference Guide* for your exam.

   The *USGBC Reference Guides* are comprehensive, but they give too much information. For example, *The LEED 2009 Reference Guide for Green Building Design and Construction (BD&C)* has about 700 oversized pages. Many of the calculations in the books are too detailed for the exam. They are also expensive (approximately $200 each, so most people may not buy them for their personal use, but instead, will seek to share an office copy).

   It is good to read a reference guide from cover to cover if you have the time. The problem is not too many people have time to read the whole reference guide. Even if you do read the whole guide, you may not remember the important issues to pass the LEED exam. You need to reread the material several times before you can remember much of it.

   Reading the reference guide from cover to cover without a guidebook is a difficult and inefficient way of preparing for the LEED AP Exam, because you do NOT know what USGBC and GBCI are looking for in the exam.

2. The USGBC workshops and related handouts are concise, but they do not cover extra credits (exemplary performance). The workshops are expensive, costing approximately $450 each.

3. Various books published by a third party are available on Amazon, bn.com and books.google.com. However, most of them are not very helpful.

   There are many books on LEED, but not all are useful.

   LEED Exam Guides series will fill in the blanks and become a valuable, reliable source:

   a. They will give you more information for your money. Each of the books in the LEED Exam Guides series has more information than the related USGBC workshops.

   b. They are exam-oriented and more effective than the USGBC reference guides.

   c. They are better than most, if not all, of the other third-party books. They give you comprehensive study materials, sample questions and answers, mock exams and answers, and critical information on building LEED certification and going green. Other third-party books only give you a fraction of the information.

   d. They are comprehensive yet concise. They are small and easy to carry around. You can read them whenever you have a few extra minutes.

   e. They are great timesavers. I have highlighted the important information that you need to understand and MEMORIZE. I also make some acronyms and short sentences to help you easily remember the credit names.

It should take you about 1 or 2 weeks of full-time study to pass each of the LEED exams. I have met people who have spent 40 hours to study and passed the exams.

You can find sample texts and other information on the LEED Exam Guides series in customer discussion sections under each of my book's listing on Amazon, bn.com and books.google.com.

What others are saying about *LEED GA Exam Guide* (Book 2, LEED Exam Guide series):

"Finally! A comprehensive study tool for LEED GA Prep!

"I took the 1-day Green LEED GA course and walked away with a power point binder printed in very small print—which was missing MUCH of the required information (although I didn't know it at the time). I studied my little heart out and took the test, only to fail it by 1 point. Turns out I did NOT study all the material I needed to in order to pass the test. I found this book, read it, marked it up, retook the test, and passed it with a 95%. Look, we all know the LEED GA exam is new and the resources for study are VERY limited. This one is the VERY best out there right now. I highly recommend it."
—ConsultantVA

"Complete overview for the LEED GA exam

"I studied this book for about 3 days and passed the exam … if you are truly interested in learning about the LEED system and green building design, this is a great place to start."
—K.A. Evans

"A Wonderful Guide for the LEED GA Exam

"After deciding to take the LEED Green Associate exam, I started to look for the best possible study materials and resources. From what I thought would be a relatively easy task, it turned into a tedious endeavor. I realized that there are vast amounts of third-party guides and handbooks. Since the official sites offer little to no help, it became clear to me that my best chance to succeed and pass this exam would be to find the most comprehensive study guide that would not only teach me the topics, but would also give me a great background and understanding of what LEED actually is. Once I stumbled upon Mr. Chen's book, all my needs were answered. This is a great study guide that will give the reader the most complete view of the LEED exam and all that it entails.

"The book is written in an easy-to-understand language and brings up great examples, tying the material to the real world. The information is presented in a coherent and logical way, which optimizes the learning process and does not go into details that will not be needed for the LEED Green Associate Exam, as many other guides do. This book stays dead on topic and keeps the reader interested in the material.

"I highly recommend this book to anyone that is considering the LEED Green Associate Exam. I learned a great deal from this guide, and I am feeling very confident about my chances for passing my upcoming exam."
—Pavel Geystrin

"Easy to read, easy to understand

"I have read through the book once and found it to be the perfect study guide for me. The author does a great job of helping you get into the right frame of mind for the content of the exam. I had started by studying the Green Building Design and Construction reference guide for LEED projects produced by the USGBC. That was the wrong approach, simply too much information with very little retention. At 636 pages in textbook format, it would have been a daunting task to get through it. Gang Chen breaks down the points, helping to minimize the amount of information but maximizing the content I was able to absorb. I plan on going through the book a few more times, and I now believe I have the right information to pass the LEED Green Associate Exam."
—Brian Hochstein

"All in one—LEED GA prep material

"Since the LEED Green Associate exam is a newer addition by USGBC, there is not much information regarding study material for this exam. When I started looking around for material, I got really confused about what material I should buy. This LEED GA guide by Gang Chen is an answer to all my worries! It is a very precise book with lots of information, like how to approach the exam, what to study and what to skip, links to online material, and tips and tricks for passing the exam. It is like the 'one stop shop' for the LEED Green Associate Exam. I think this book can also be a good reference guide for green building professionals. A must-have!"
—SwatiD

"An ESSENTIAL LEED GA Exam Reference Guide

"This book is an invaluable tool in preparation for the LEED Green Associate (GA) Exam. As a practicing professional in the consulting realm, I found this book to be all-inclusive of the preparatory material needed for sitting the exam. The information provides clarity to the fundamental and advanced concepts of what LEED aims to achieve. A tremendous benefit is the connectivity of the concepts with real-world applications.

"The author, Gang Chen, provides a vast amount of knowledge in a very clear, concise, and logical media. For those that have not picked up a textbook in a while, it is very manageable to extract the needed information from this book. If you are taking the exam, do yourself a favor and purchase a copy of this great guide. Applicable fields: Civil Engineering, Architectural Design, MEP, and General Land Development."
—Edwin L. Tamang

Note: Other books in the **LEED Exam Guides series** are in the process of being produced. At least **one book will eventually be produced for each of the LEED exams.** The series include:

LEED v4 Green Associate Exam Guide (LEED GA): *Comprehensive Study Materials, Sample Questions, Mock Exam, Green Building LEED Certification, and Sustainability*, LEED Exam Guide series, ArchiteG.com. Latest Edition.

LEED GA MOCK EXAMS (LEED v4): *Questions, Answers, and Explanations: A Must-Have for the LEED Green Associate Exam, Green Building LEED Certification, and Sustainability*, LEED Exam Guide series, ArchiteG.com. Latest Edition

LEED v4 BD&C EXAM GUIDE: A Must-Have for the LEED AP BD+C Exam: Comprehensive Study Materials, Sample Questions, Mock Exam, Green Building Design and Construction, LEED Certification, and Sustainability, LEED Exam Guide series, ArchiteG.com. Latest Edition.

LEED v4 BD&C MOCK EXAMS: Questions, Answers, and Explanations: A Must-Have for the LEED AP BD+C Exam, Green Building LEED Certification, and Sustainability, LEED Exam Guide series, ArchiteG.com. Latest Edition.

LEED ID&C Exam Guide: A Must-Have for the LEED AP ID+C Exam: Study Materials, Sample Questions, Green Interior Design and Construction, Green Building LEED Certification, and Sustainability, LEED Exam Guide series, ArchiteG.com. Latest Edition.

LEED ID&C Mock Exam: Questions, Answers, and Explanations: A Must-Have for the LEED AP ID+C Exam, Green Interior Design and Construction, Green Building LEED Certification, and Sustainability, LEED Exam Guide series, ArchiteG.com. Latest Edition.

LEED O&M MOCK EXAMS: Questions, Answers, and Explanations: A Must-Have for the LEED O&M Exam, Green Building LEED Certification, and Sustainability, LEED Exam Guide series, ArchiteG.com. Latest Edition.

LEED O&M EXAM GUIDE: A Must-Have for the LEED AP O+M Exam: Comprehensive Study Materials, Sample Questions, Mock Exam, Green Building Operations and Maintenance, LEED Certification, and Sustainability, LEED Exam Guide series, ArchiteG.com. Latest Edition.

LEED HOMES EXAM GUIDE: A Must-Have for the LEED AP Homes Exam: Comprehensive Study Materials, Sample Questions, Mock Exam, Green Building LEED Certification, and Sustainability, LEED Exam Guide series, ArchiteG.com. Latest Edition.

LEED ND EXAM GUIDE: A Must-Have for the LEED AP Neighborhood Development Exam: Comprehensive Study Materials, Sample Questions, Mock Exam, Green Building LEED Certification, and Sustainability, LEED Exam Guide series, ArchiteG.com. Latest Edition.

How to order these books:
You can order the books listed above at:
http://www.GreenExamEducation.com

OR
http://www.ArchiteG.com

Building Construction

Project Management, Construction Administration, Drawings, Specs, Detailing Tips, Schedules, Checklists, and Secrets Others Don't Tell You (Architectural Practice Simplified, 2nd edition)

Learn the Tips, Become One of Those Who Know Building Construction and Architectural Practice, and Thrive!

For architectural practice and building design and construction industry, there are two kinds of people: those who know, and those who don't. The tips of building design and construction and project management have been undercover—until now.

Most of the existing books on building construction and architectural practice are too expensive, too complicated, and too long to be practical and helpful. This book simplifies the process to make it easier to understand and uncovers the tips of building design and construction and project management. It sets up a solid foundation and fundamental framework for this field. It covers every aspect of building construction and architectural practice in plain and concise language and introduces it to all people. Through practical case studies, it demonstrates the efficient and proper ways to handle various issues and problems in architectural practice and building design and construction industry.

It is for ordinary people and aspiring young architects as well as seasoned professionals in the construction industry. For ordinary people, it uncovers the tips of building construction; for aspiring architects, it works as a construction industry survival guide and a guidebook to shorten the process in mastering architectural practice and climbing up the professional ladder; for seasoned architects, it has many checklists to refresh their memory. It is an indispensable reference book for ordinary people, architectural students, interns, drafters, designers, seasoned architects, engineers, construction administrators, superintendents, construction managers, contractors, and developers.

You will learn:
1. How to develop your business and work with your client.
2. The entire process of building design and construction, including programming, entitlement, schematic design, design development, construction documents, bidding, and construction administration.
3. How to coordinate with governing agencies, including a county's health department and a city's planning, building, fire, public works departments, etc.
4. How to coordinate with your consultants, including soils, civil, structural, electrical, mechanical, plumbing engineers, landscape architects, etc.
5. How to create and use your own checklists to do quality control of your construction documents.
6. How to use various logs (i.e., RFI log, submittal log, field visit log, etc.) and lists (contact list, document control list, distribution list, etc.) to organize and simplify your work.
7. How to respond to RFI, issue CCDs, review change orders, submittals, etc.
8. How to make your architectural practice a profitable and successful business.

Planting Design Illustrated
A Must-Have for Landscape Architecture: A Holistic Garden Design Guide with Architectural and Horticultural Insight, and Ideas from Famous Gardens in Major Civilizations

One of the most significant books on landscaping!

This is one of the most comprehensive books on planting design. It fills in the blanks of the field and introduces poetry, painting, and symbolism into planting design. It covers in detail the two major systems of planting design: formal planting design and naturalistic planting design. It has numerous line drawings and photos to illustrate the planting design concepts and principles. Through in-depth discussions of historical precedents and practical case studies, it uncovers the fundamental design principles and concepts, as well as the underpinning philosophy for planting design. It is an indispensable reference book for landscape architecture students, designers, architects, urban planners, and ordinary garden lovers.

What Others Are Saying about *Planting Design Illustrated* ...

"I found this book to be absolutely fascinating. You will need to concentrate while reading it, but the effort will be well worth your time."
—Bobbie Schwartz, former president of APLD (Association of Professional Landscape Designers) and author of *The Design Puzzle: Putting the Pieces Together*.

"This is a book that you have to read, and it is more than well worth your time. Gang Chen takes you well beyond what you will learn in other books about basic principles like color, texture, and mass."
—Jane Berger, editor & publisher of gardendesignonline

"As a longtime consumer of gardening books, I am impressed with Gang Chen's inclusion of new information on planting design theory for Chinese and Japanese gardens. Many gardening books discuss the beauty of Japanese gardens, and a few discuss the unique charms of Chinese gardens, but this one explains how Japanese and Chinese history, as well as geography and artistic traditions, bear on the development of each country's style. The material on traditional Western garden planting is thorough and inspiring, too. *Planting Design Illustrated* definitely rewards repeated reading and study. Any garden designer will read it with profit."
—Jan Whitner, editor of the *Washington Park Arboretum Bulletin*

"Enhanced with an annotated bibliography and informative appendices, *Planting Design Illustrated* offers an especially "reader friendly" and practical guide that makes it a very strongly recommended addition to personal, professional, academic, and community library gardening & landscaping reference collection and supplemental reading list."
—Midwest Book Review

"Where to start? *Planting Design Illustrated* is, above all, fascinating and refreshing! Not something the lay reader encounters every day, the book presents an unlikely topic in an easily digestible, easy-to-follow way. It is superbly organized with a comprehensive table of contents, bibliography, and appendices. The writing, though expertly informative, maintains its accessibility throughout and is a joy to read. The detailed and beautiful illustrations expanding on the concepts presented were my favorite portion. One of the finest books I've encountered in this contest in the past 5 years."
—**Writer's Digest 16th Annual International Self-Published Book Awards Judge's Commentary**

"The work in my view has incredible application to planting design generally and a system approach to what is a very difficult subject to teach, at least in my experience. Also featured is a very beautiful philosophy of garden design principles bordering poetry. It's my strong conviction that this work needs to see the light of day by being published for the use of professionals, students & garden enthusiasts."
—**Donald C. Brinkerhoff, FASLA, chairman and CEO of Lifescapes International, Inc.**

Index

Made in the
USA
Columbia, SC